Australian Flower Essences
for the
21st Century

Note to readers:
Information in this book is not intended as a substitute for professional health care treatment.

First published in 1997
Australasian Flower Essence Academy
P.O. Box 355 Scarborough, WA 6016, Australia
Telephone: 61 8 9443 5600 Facsimile: 61 8 9443 5610
Internet Website: Livingessences.com.au

Photographs by Vasudeva and Kadambii Barnao.
Start's Spider Orchid photograph by Bill Jackson.

National Library of Australia
Cataloguing in publication information:

Barnao, Vasudeva, 1951 -
Barnao, Kadambii, 1958 -
   Australian Flower Essences for the 21st Century.

   Bibliography.
   ISBN 0 646 34324 6

Designed and produced by Acorn Design,
Perth, Western Australia Telephone: 61 8 9381 3113
Printed by Advance Press

Australian Flower Essences
for the
21st Century

Vasudeva and Kadambii Barnao

AUSTRALASIAN FLOWER ESSENCE ACADEMY

Perth, Australia.

CONTENTS

CONTENTS

This book is dedicated to all those who live to make life better for others, who appreciate the beauty of Life, in humans, animals, plants, and all other collective and individual life-forms.

Our heart felt thanks go to all the staff, students, research practitioners, friends and colleagues at the Academy, whose dedication and support has enhanced the work, ensuring that the wildflowers will find their way to people in need in the 21st Century.

Vasudeva and Kadambii both regard the start of their explorations with flower essences was the development, over many decades, of their knowledge and practice of Yogic sciences. Before they met each other they had both been practicing spiritual meditation for many years, which they credit with giving them the intuitive sensitivity and inner quiet to appreciate the subtleties of human nature and the many mysterious aspects of the flowers.

Vasudeva first began to work with researching and producing Australian flower essences in 1977, as part of his general interest in natural health practices. He had studied several disciplines, and although greatly helped by them physically, always felt the causes had not been defined or dealt with. He was surprised by the effects of the flower essences, and the way they moved in the consciousness and manifested inner and outer well being. He saw the potential for helping common human difficulties with the flower essences as vitally important.

In 1980 he moved from Sydney, to Perth, in the heart of the Wildflower State of Western Australia. There he met and married Kadambii and together they began a great expansion of research and development of flower essences and the education programmes, at their Australasian Flower Essence Academy, to spread their use.

In the late eighties Kadambii's work with an aboriginal community led to the discovery of the oldest living tradition of flower essence therapy, that of the Nyoongah people. From the elder, Nunjin, they learned that their research was ratified by the ancient practices.

Later they also discovered the ancient Buddhist tradition of flower essence therapy, from Malaysia and Thailand, where temples specialize in flower essence healing.

They pioneered the research and use of flower essences through acu-points and meridians, and this and their development of flower essences into creams and lotions led to their work being taught and utilized in hospitals.

From 1989 to the present, the years have seen much travelling and lecturing at medical and natural health conferences, and seminars for Academy students world-wide. To help students nationally and internationally, Kadambii and Vasudeva created the Video Correspondence course, and the Walkabout Healing video.

In 1995 Kadambii and Vasudeva were invested as knights Hospitaller of Saint John of Jerusalem, Knights of Malta, a nine hundred year old international order of philanthropists.

They live in Perth, Australia with their three children.

Flowers attract Life to them. This is the secret behind the forms, colours, scents and consciousness that they manifest. The desire to interact with Life and to break through the limitations of present states of evolution is a desire we share with the floral kingdom.

Humans and flowers are in the midst of a love affair that has been flourishing for hundreds of thousands of years. Even in the graves of the Neanderthal pre- humans flowers were strewn. Why did they feel the need to do this? In which way do we feel that flowers help us with the many rites of passage in our lives, of births, marriages, worship, celebrations, sickness and death? Even in every mundane sphere, from prints on clothes and curtains to paper bags and soap, everywhere we draw to us the images of the flowers.

Perhaps we need only to imagine a world without flowers to recognize what part flowers play in our lives. The gardens, parks and wildernesses that we seek to replenish our spirit and clear our minds and to invigorate ourselves, these are the settings for our interactions with the flowers, and are precious to us.

Nyoongah aboriginal people of the South-West of Australia lived surrounded by the prolific and year round blossoming of wildflowers today renowned by botanists the world over. Little wonder that the ancient custodians of the wildflower country hold the oldest living tradition of flower essence therapy. The Mobarn or Wadinyoongahri, as leaders and healers of the tribe, would conduct a healing ceremony where a person was laid in a pit of earth-covered coals, over which was sprinkled water and flowers, with a kangaroo skin laid on top in a type of sauna. It was considered that the

person would get a new spirit from the flowers. A person who was afraid would gain courage, an angry person would find peace, a sick person would become well.This is what we are attracted to in the presence of flowers, the enhancing of our lives through interacting with the gifts of their healing nature.

For the Nyoongah, the flowers carried the colours of the Creator Spirit, the Waugal, or Rainbow Snake, after he pierced the ice age covering the world and enabled the Sun woman to penetrate with her warmth. The flowers in all the colours of the rainbow remind them of how Life was restored.

In many cultures the subtle use of flowers, the flower essence, has come and gone, and now has come again.

In a very personal sense for us, the authors, the gifts of the wildflowers have been so important as to have saved us from serious illnesses, have been a catalyst for inner growth and present us with mysteries that will nourish research for the rest of our lives. The development of Living Essences of Australia, from 1977 onwards has been a revelation for us on every personal and professional level. Our research into the flowers and how to access their healing potentials for health and well-being has led to the development of particular diagnostic and application techniques, and these in turn have become our education programme at the Academy, and part of courses for naturopathic schools and medical staff in hospitals.

Our first focus was to provide an education programme for those who wanted to specialize in flower essence therapy. The one year course was established at the Academy in 1985, and every year the course expanded until by 1989 the five year set course was finalized.

Our aim was to give people the opportunity to be able to practice effectively the wide range of flower essence healing skills, as a total healing discipline in its own right. We believed that there was a great need for experts in this field, who could deal with the real and immediate health needs of the community. Prior to this we found that flower essence therapy was considered only as a side line to other natural or esoteric therapies and the full scope of its potential was never reached. Therapists would "throw a few flower essences in" with their other health therapies, just to see if it would help, or at best, use flower essences to relieve mental distress in the short term. The education programme at the Academy is fulfilling our wish for more flower essence therapists to be working in the community. Every year a hundred more people graduate at the 1st year therapist level alone, through the courses at Perth headquarters and through the national and international video correspondence courses. This book represents the curriculum for the first year course.

More advanced knowledge and areas of the senior curriculum, which include esoteric sciences, are scheduled for books following this one. Some of these expanded areas are; the journey of the mind through the meridians (this includes the psychology of meridians and acu-points), archetypal psychology diagnosis, astrological diagnosis, the metaphysical aspects of flower essences, the science of the Chakras and the evolution of consciousness.

Throughout all the years of our research we have felt it was important for flower essences to be able to reach their full potential within every area of healing. So to be able to use flower essences in different healing settings, and to work alongside other healing disciplines, specific uses have been refined. To enable other therapists and health professionals to use flower essences in their field with confidence, systems and methods of application are clearly defined and taught in a way that addresses their needs and those of their patients.

With all of this has always been the need to have simple and effective systems that the general public could access for their everyday well being and health. This was the inspiration behind research in 1984 on the use of flower essences in creams for pain, stress and arthritis. The effectiveness of these new methods of application actually commenced the progress of the flower essences into the hospital setting. Later the combinations of essences for oral dosage in the Wildflower Relief Elixir, and 21st Century Survival Kit were developed and released.

During all this time we were finding more healing flowers as we spent time in the field, in forests, desserts, on the kwongon sandplains, in the gorges, on the beaches and mountains. In some real way we cannot help but feel that our work has been creating a bridge between these natural worlds and the worlds of humans, so beset in their modern dilemmas. Perhaps this is a very apt description of what flower essence therapy does generally, bridging the gap between a person and the natural balance of their original bearing.

The journey of healing discovery will always deeply engage all aspects of a human being. With flower essences, the healing of the physical, mental and spiritual is addressed so gently yet definitively. It is then compelling to use the wisdom gained to relieve the suffering of others. We hope that in sharing our knowledge from the past two decades with the readers of this book, we can help more flowers and people find each other and enjoy the wonders of healing and restoration.

Vasudeva and Kadambii

There has not been, so far on this planet, either a perfect human society or a perfect healing system. This perfection is a goal that has seemed out of reach. Human history is one of self discovery as we have sought this prize, with knowledge gained ever to be exchanged, or altered by, more recent discoveries.

Some scientific progress has been involved in the deeper aspects of the human being and the workings of consciousness and energy. Many ancient and traditional societies worked with these sciences for thousands of years and have handed down valuable understandings of the workings of Life, and how we can utilize this knowledge for the health and well being of all. The terminology was certainly different, and often misunderstood in today's frame of reference. Some of this knowledge was also lost in superstitious dogma and religion, becoming useless.

Other scientific progress has been focused primarily on the more external aspects of the human being, from the gross physical to subtle molecular, atomic and sub atomic physical levels. These sciences have brought many benefits to humanity, though often, during the developmental process, much harm was also done to humans and their environment. Many of the scientific practices we see today will be regarded by future societies in the same way we now retrospectively view the lack of hygiene and hand washing by surgeons a hundred years ago.

This is already happening. A parallel practice to the lack of hand washing of yesteryear is the common practice today of not examining the deeper causes of illness and mental problems when a person needs healing. People in human society are now demanding Holistic medicine, that takes into account all of their being not just the basic physical component. They also want the best physical result without harmful side effects.

The healing for the 21st Century will have to understand deeply the human mind, the journeys individuals make in their life, what they are striving for and the effects this has on them. The healing will have to be both subtle enough to deal with our finest being, and yet be practical and relieve physical suffering. It will also have to be clearly explained.

The wildflowers offer this wide range of healing, and combined with diagnostic techniques, also help to uncover the many layers upon which suffering is built. In other words, the person receiving healing also learns about their inner nature and how they got to the point of needing healing. Such wisdom is invaluable for building a better life, and preventing further suffering.

Modern life-styles do not often give the time and space for the type of healing we require, and the intensity of modern life speeds up reactions on the mind/body/spirit of individuals. If we cannot go to the forest to restore our balance we can seek Nature in the flower essences always within our reach.

Healing Mind Patterns

The wildflowers' work can be from the physical level filtering back to relieve the mind state which caused it, or from the mind state filtering down to relieve the physical. If, for example, a person has back pain caused by tension, then the flower essences can be used topically or on floral acu-points to relieve the physical symptoms. Dampiera essence could be chosen because the pain was in the form of tension. However the essences would build up an effect on the mind, where the tension was being projected and maintained. Eventually the mind would be healed of the tension and stop producing the pain symptom in the body. Similarly a person who was often in a tense state of mind, and the tension showed up in painful back muscles, could be treated with an oral dose of Dampiera to heal the mind of the tense thought projections that were causing the physical symptoms.

The aim, in both cases, is to go to the root of the problem lying in the person's mind, or to where the attitude was affecting the body, according to whether they conceive of the mind element, or only perceive the physical symptom. Floral acu-pressure speeds up the physical response to the healing message, this is why the combination of specific wildflower essences with specific acu-points has been a breakthrough for flower essence therapy in general. However for permanent healing, time is required, and the administration of the essence on acu-points, or orally, should progress past the physical symptom stage. The people who find that they have now grown out of the mind pattern to tense up about their life, have completed the healing circle which the Dampiera began.

Understanding Ourselves To Heal Ourselves

Of course as the specialty of flower essences is healing consciousness, most of the diagnosing is focused on the mind itself. The diagnostic techniques we have developed, and which are explained in this book, help a person self diagnose or be able to facilitate another person's self diagnosis.

To be in charge of our own healing is important in many ways. Firstly we are not blindly handing over our responsibility and power so that someone will deliver us from our body or mind. By choosing to understand how we came to be in discomfort of mind or body we actively participate in the process of healing from the beginning to the completion. Secondly, we can gain knowledge about ourselves, others, and Life in general by working actively with the process of healing. Thirdly, we can prevent further problems for ourselves and even help others with their problems with the wisdom gained on the journey of healing with flower essences.

Basically what we are diagnosing with flower essence techniques are the nature of a brick wall we are facing in our lives. This is usually a situation and accompanying emotions that are continually being repeated. We often find that we are not fully successful in the ways we try to resolve a problem. It is easy to make the mistake of thinking that the problem is beyond our power to resolve.

What usually happens is we try to break the wall with the same old blunt instrument time and again. We may try to be more patient to resolve a personal problem, or more angry, harden ourselves, or run away from it, only to find the same situation returns again, if not with the same person then with others or just ourselves.

The healing must come from within, the mind is its own brick wall. The brick wall is made up of set mind patterns, inherently ours and developed over time.

Every experience we have lived through has left an impression on us. If the experience has been painful then we have also built a thought form around it, a survival concept, so we can try to avoid the pain the next time. So if we are hurt by being close to someone, in our next relationship the survival concept will try to stop us from being close enough to get hurt. Now it is easy to see that the survival concept has become a pattern of living that will stop us from enjoying intimacy.

So many of these concepts clog up our minds, and yet they have been part of our very survival. To heal our mind is to regain free will, objective decision making, and spontaneity, essential to happiness and quality of Life.

The nature of the wildflowers is to heal the brick walls of our mind and allow us to go forward to new pathways in Life, to restore us to the vigour and inspiration about living which is our birth right.

The new awakening of human consciousness to its birthright is the mark of the age in which we live. Our natural inclination to try to break through the limitations on any level of our existence and expand our minds has lead to a thirst for more understanding and knowledge of Life. The greatest realization has been so obvious, that we are a ***part*** of Life, sheltered and nurtured within Life, and not outside of all other Life.

As we heal and break the bondages of our mind, we become free to explore our spiritual nature and relationship to the Universe. Our small mind can start to access the Universal mind and see the very nature of Nature. This is the domain of the 21st Century, and the human, whole and healed, deep within its being, will surely extend into a great evolutionary leap forward.

This book has been divided into sections for ease of finding and using information. After the introduction and foundation chapter on Healing for the 21st Century come the first "how to" sections. These describe diagnostic and application techniques which show the range of ways in which the wildflower essences can be used to maximize their healing properties.

Diagnostic Techniques for Flower Essence Therapy

1. Psychological Profile

2. Flower Affinity Diagnosis (includes colour groupings)

3. Baihui Diagnosis

4. Floral Acu-points

Application Techniques for Flower Essence Therapy

1. Oral Dosages

2. Floral Acu-points, Floral Acu-pressure

3. Flower Essence Projector

4. Topical Application
   (Direct application and; Body Work, Chiropractic/Osteopathy, Physiotherapy etc.)

5. Baths

6. Sprays

7. Meditations

Wildflowers from A to Z

The main body of the book is the wildflowers themselves and the individual healing values they hold. These values are categorized under sections or headings for each flower as follows:

Axioms

Under the common and botanical name of each flower is a short phrase which is a condensed concept of the healing properties.
(These are also listed in an index at the back of the book)

Healing Definition

Beneath the Axiom is the condensed healing definition of the flower.

Positive Qualities - Key Words

To the side of the wildflower picture are words which are associated with the healing properties of the flower. These words were chosen to help with identifying the values a person is seeking in their healing.
(These are also listed in an index at the back of the book)

Problem Target - Key Words

Below the positive quality key words are the key words that help in identifying the problem, or state of mind associated with the problem to which the healing properties of this particular wildflower relate.
(These are also listed in an index at the back of the book)

Physical - Common Uses

For some flowers common uses for physical problems are listed. The essence is either used in simple topical application, oral doses, in baths or sprays. These application techniques are explained in the front section of the book (Pg 46). (Physical symptoms are listed in an index at the back of the book)

Physical - Floral Acu-pressure

For some flowers there are specific acu-points to which they can be applied for physical problems. The list of physical symptoms is to help in the correct selection of the essence. Some acu-points have references to other flowers used either (a) together with the flower given or (b) instead of the flower given. Selection of the correct flower is then made by reading the psychological profile under Mind - Floral Acu-pressure of each flower, and discerning the mind state, and therefore the flower, that is most relevant to the person. The acu-points and the application of essences on those points are explained in the front of the book (Pgs 40 & 44). (Physical symptoms are listed in an index at the back of the book)

Mind - Common Uses

Under this heading, common uses for each wildflower essence for mind states are given with further explanation to the condensed healing definition. At the end of this section a summary of common healing results is also given. The essence is taken orally in this common uses section.

Mind - Floral Acu-pressure

This section gives the psychological profile, or the mind state which is related to the use of the acu-point described. It can be related to the physical symptoms in the Physical - Acu-pressure section, but not necessarily.

Healing Journey of the Soul

There are three aspects of healing taken into account in this book, that of the physical, the mind and the Soul. We can all readily understand what physical suffering is and what it feels like to have relief from it. We can all concur how disillusionment, weaknesses, unattainable goals, relationship problems or negative states of mind cause us suffering, and how great is it to be helped out of them. But what is meant by help for the Soul?

The term "holistic", used for natural and humanistic health practices over the last decades, has taken into account the necessary integration of body and mind for optimum health and happiness. Is this enough? What more can be aspired to?

The spiritual aspect can mean many things to many people. Our interpretation is that the spiritual expression of the Soul, when expressed in Life, is one where collective welfare is enhanced by the individual recognizing their place in the Universal whole. Although the individual journey of the Soul has its own personal dimensions and fulfillment, its progress towards spiritual goals throws light onto everything around it. This progress is at the enhancement of, not at the expense of, all other Life. This is in contrast to the progress towards desires of the mind and its more exclusive focus of individuality. The personal transitory fulfilments of the mind can be the source of much personal and planetary suffering. Human beings, out of touch with their Soul which recognizes its kinship with All Things, focus on personal desires which can destroy Eco-systems, relationships, and, as a consequence, their own physical and mental health.

The "Healing Pathway of the Soul" section with each wildflower, reveals the help that a particular flower essence gives to the development of the spiritual journey, and offers deeper insights into the flower's potential use for those wanting to work on spiritual aspirations.

For example, on the personal level, the *Mauve Melaleuca* helps the mind to consolidate and generate its own foundation of Love from within. This enables a person to feel content whether they are being loved by someone else or not. On the Soul level, the lessons of seeking deeper and deeper sources of Love are an integral part of spirituality. *Mauve Melaleuca* helps us to get past the obstacles of the mind so we may go deeper and experience the joys of the Universal Love which is the basis of all Life.

Meditation Poem

The last section for each flower is the meditation poem. While each poem holds the healing essence of a particular wildflower it is also a tool in bringing the healing wisdom to the mind. Meditation is a process of focusing the mind on a point of ideation. In the case of a flower essence meditation, the focus is the healing attributes of the flower which bring transformations and expansions in consciousness. A method of flower meditation is described in the front section of the book. (see Pg 51)

For the Animals

Finally, in the last part of the book, an over view of the use of the wildflowers for animal welfare is described.

The following diagnostic techniques have been developed at the Academy and are part of the education programme. Any or all of them can be used at one time for self diagnosis or, for a therapist's diagnosis of a client.

1. PSYCHOLOGICAL PROFILE

The bringing together of the right flower or flowers with the person who needs them is the basic aim of flower essence therapy. The more accurately this is done the more defined the healing result. The primary method of choosing specific flowers for a person and their specific needs is the matching of the psychological profile of the person with the healing definition of the flowers.

This method relies on a number of factors, for example, how well a person understands the problems they are facing. It is often much easier to diagnose when there are physical symptoms which reveal sources of problems. For example, if a person suffers from tight shoulder, neck and chest muscles then one would be assessing which of the attitudes they hold produce this effect in the body. However if the problem is one of general feelings of unhappiness, discontent or unease, and the person cannot define exactly where the feelings originate one must delve deeper.

It can be difficult to have clarity with problems and situations in your life when you are in the middle of them, however, there is a way of seeing through the maze. Ask yourself a few questions:

What is the brick wall I am facing in my life at present, and what part of my nature is making this happen or making the situation harder to resolve?

What is the problem that keeps repeating itself in my life, and what part of my nature needs to change so that I don't have to go through this again?

What change in attitude or behaviour would be most beneficial to me at present, but which I feel is difficult or impossible to achieve?

When these questions are answered it is easier to select the flowers for the central issues that are limiting the potential for your fulfillment and well being.

This brings us to the second factor in the psychological profile method of choosing the right flower essence - an objective and honest assessment. When living with a difficulty or problem we find many factors, external and internal are involved. We have to come to terms with the day to day effects of this situation on us, and so arrive at set ideas about the nature of the problem. Often this means we focus on external realities, like, "if only things weren't like this, then I wouldn't feel like that. I would be happy

25

then." If we wait for the world, or people in it, to change before we claim our happiness we will be waiting a long time.

The basic reality is that we cannot dictate to Life. People and situations are outside the realm of our personal mastery - but the good news is that in any situation we can have mastery over ourselves, and thus choose which way OUR life goes. This area is the specialty of flower essences. The best result we can get with flower essences is in direct relation to the amount of objective and honest assessment we have of ourselves in choosing the flower essences we need.

The other factor in choosing the right flower essences for healing is knowing the flower essences well. For those who have not as yet become familiar with the many helpful flowers, this book will give you the introductions you need. The various headings and sections for the wildflowers themselves and the other diagnostic techniques have been chosen to help pin point the crucial healing properties that people seek. Once selection is made the application technique is then chosen, whether to take the essences in oral dose, as a floral acu-pressure treatment, as a bath or spray therapy and perhaps add a meditation exercise.

2. *FLOWER AFFINITY DIAGNOSIS*

Movement in Life seems to be motivated by the forces of attraction and repulsion, with a slice of neutral no-man's land in between. We make efforts towards that which we desire and try to avoid those things that make us uncomfortable or sad, taking both directions with equal vigour. We find ourselves sometimes between these two factors in a systaltic pause.

When we are drawn to go out into a park, or into a forest or wilderness, what pulls us there? We walk, lie down to rest, or sit and contemplate. When flowers are there we are drawn to them, but interestingly, more to some than to others. Just like the animals when they are sick, we instinctually seek in nature that which will ease our suffering. Animals don't have a microscope with which to analyze what they want, and in this technological age we often bypass our same important intuitive responses. Indigenous healers made a point of honouring subconscious responses and urges as signposts to the inner workings of a person. These urges are what lie behind the effectiveness of Flower Affinity Diagnosis.

You may recall a flower from your childhood, at your house, at your grandma's, on the way to school or where you had your holidays. There will often be an atmosphere that comes with the memory of this flower, whether it is a happy or painful memory. The flower you recall, whatever atmosphere comes with it, was one which you were subconsciously drawn to, were interacting with and being helped by.

This is also true about the flowers we choose for our gardens. We assume that we must like all flowers, but if that was true we would find it impossible to choose which ones to plant in our garden. Instead we find it easy to choose whatever we most want, taking into account, of course, what will best thrive in the conditions of sun and soil.

If we consider flowers we have always loved, then we may also remember some which we really were attracted to but which now, although appreciated, do not seem so special to us. This denotes a "moving on" in our life from the problem or attitudes we had when that flower seemed to be so strongly attractive to us.

There are three common responses a person has to a flower:

1.   A positive attraction which feels uplifting and encouraging.

2.   A neutral response that has little impact.

3.   A negative response that is uncomfortable or irritating.

The positive attraction shows that we are open to and feel a need for the healing which this flower radiates. In this case the flower seems to help us with a change or state of mind we are consciously striving for, engendering a sense of positivity, serenity or carefreeness.

The neutral response shows that the issues which this flower deals with are not needed. Although pleasant, the flower is not strongly interacting with our state of mind.

The negative response shows that we are uncomfortable with the strong interaction we are having with a flower. The flower is definitely a healer for the state of mind we have, bringing up thoughts we wish would stay silent. Sometimes this is simply because of a painful memory associated with a particular state of mind. Other times the repulsion is because we find it hard to face a negative state within ourselves and do not want to be reminded of it. This negative response can be seen as a negative attraction.

The Flower Affinity Diagnostic technique is a way to use our three basic responses to flowers in selecting the appropriate essence for our healing.

The steps are as follows:

BASIC METHOD OF FLOWER AFFINITY DIAGNOSIS

1. Concentrate on a particular problem or situation you are experiencing which undermines the quality of your Life. Get in touch with all the feelings and atmospheres that this situation evokes. The stronger your fix on the emotions involved, the clearer the diagnosis will be. Sometimes it helps to go over a particular situation from the past that typifies the problem, and replay it a number of times in your mind.

2. Now that the feelings, or undesirable state of mind has been evoked the second step can begin. Holding these feelings, go through the flower pictures one by one, looking at the picture at a steady and reasonably quick pace. You want a subconscious response not a conscious one, hence the need for a good pace that doesn't allow much intellectual choice making. (We use a Flower Affinity Deck of Photos at the Academy (from whence they can be obtained), however the photos of this book can also be used by turning the pages to each wildflower at a steady pace)

3. Make a note of any flower to which you have a strong response, either positively or negatively, always keeping the problem and atmosphere in your mind. Put any flowers you had a neutral response to on one side, they will not be needed.

4. Once you have made your choices and noted them as negative or positive, select the seven flowers which have evoked the strongest impact and interaction, numbering them from one to seven.

5. Some flowers may have been subconsciously chosen because they reflect the behaviour of a person, or people, directly involved in your situation. You may feel the flower does not apply to you personally. However, the seed-shadow is likely to be within yourself.

A woman may choose the Red Leschenaultia flower, which heals states of harshness and insensitivity. She cannot understand why she would choose this flower, she is already very caring and sensitive in her relationship with an uncaring insensitive man. However, one day, in this relationship, or maybe even one ten years hence, the woman may say to herself, "why should I be sensitive anymore", and harden herself towards others. If she doesn't resolve the issue, there is every likelihood that a manifesting of these characteristics can occur. The present attraction for the flower, indicates that the seed-shadow is in the process of being nurtured. Although seeming to be more appropriate for her partner, the flower may be becoming very appropriate for her. Also, in mastering the healing message of that flower essence, the woman gains mastery over that hardening aspect of the mind and learns to deal with such behaviour in others.

The seven flowers remaining are those which relate to the problem you chose to work with, and can be made into an oral dose, (see section in Application Techniques for Flower Essence Therapy, Oral Doses) or go on to the Baihui diagnosis technique to further experience the impact of the flowers for refined selection.

MORE ADVANCED METHODS OF FLOWER AFFINITY DIAGNOSIS

To extend the therapeutic scope of the diagnosis several other steps can be made.

If you have a Flower Affinity Diagnosis Deck; (that is, separate laminated photos of each flower)

1. After the first selection of flowers in the three categories of positive, negative and neutral, put the neutral away and lay the negatively chosen flowers on the left and the positive on the right.

2. Look at the issues the flowers represent and put them in groups, for example you may have flowers concerning self esteem, flowers concerning energy problems, flowers concerning painful memories. (The negative and positive selections will become mixed together.)

3. In seeing the flower's healing properties, look for the reaction sequences of the problem. Using the example above to demonstrate this point: the painful events may be at the centre, the self esteem issues may arise from them, and the energy problems are a consequence of these self esteem issues.

When seeing the reaction sequences of the issues with this technique, it is like making a map of our consciousness where we can see clearly the journey we have made so far in this situation, and why we are feeling certain states of mind, and states of body.

It is also common to get a reaction source which is all about our deepest desires. Often the orchids and the waterlilies point to a Life direction desire which we are yearning for, are reaching for, beyond the brick wall of our problem. Such sources are inspiring to claim consciously, realizing that although bogged down with working reality, we can work towards our inner aspirations, and thereby help speed our healing.

4. As with the basic method then proceed to choose the seven most strongly impacting flowers from all chosen so far, numbering them from one to seven. The oral dose can then be made, or further refined diagnosis can be done with the Baihui technique.

The following is an example of a Flower Affinity Diagnosis. Note that whether the flower is chosen positively or negatively it defines the state of mind of the person being diagnosed (like making a map). In the case of the positive choice the flower's healing property is something the person is consciously aware they need. The negative choice shows that the healing properties of the flower are needed, but the state of mind they are needed for is difficult for the conscious mind to face or process.

Pos. chosen	Pos. chosen
White Spider Orchid	White Nymph Waterlily

Neg. chosen	Neg. chosen	Pos. chosen
Black Kangaroo Paw	Illyarrie	Menzies Banksia

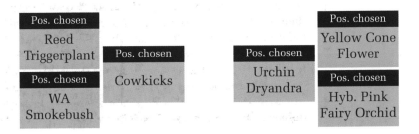

Pos. chosen		
Reed Triggerplant		Yellow Cone Flower

Pos. chosen	Pos. chosen	Pos. chosen	Pos. chosen
WA Smokebush	Cowkicks	Urchin Dryandra	Hyb. Pink Fairy Orchid

In this example the first layer of the person's aspirations are seen. The *White Spider Orchid*, positively chosen, means the person would like to be able to rise above, and master, the feelings of being overwhelmed by the suffering around them in their situation. The *White Nymph Waterlily*, positively chosen, would indicate that the state of mind they are yearning for is one where they can take a clear and benevolent perspective, seeing the overall needs of a situation, and coming from their highest consciousness to bring clarity and peace.

The second layer is about the pain of the present situation. The Illyarrie has been negatively chosen indicating that the person wants to shut out shadows of past experiences and not face them. The Menzies Banksia, positively chosen, means the person understands they are paralyzed by their pain and need to break through it. The *Black Kangaroo Paw*, negatively chosen, means they have negativity, probably towards other people involved in the situation who have hurt them, and don't like admitting they feel this way. Often this is because their higher self knows this is not a good way to handle things, and the negativity may go against deeply held beliefs. In some cases people don't like to admit to themselves how badly another person can affect them.

On the third layer, the person's self esteem has been affected by the hurt they have suffered. The *Urchin Dryandra*, positively chosen, indicates a loss of Joy, and feelings of inferiority because someone has not loved them. They need to establish their sense of self worth. This they readily acknowledge. The *Yellow Cone Flower*, positively chosen, adds to this description with the person seeking recognition from others, hoping that by being good to them they will be loved. Again the person is not valuing and honouring themselves, which they will acknowledge. The *Hybrid Pink Fairy Orchid*, positively chosen, indicates the person is aware how much they are influenced by the emotions and reactions of others, that they try to please and keep the peace, so they will be accepted. This means they go up and down with the moods of those around them, unable to feel whole or at peace.

The fourth layer is a group of flowers that deal with the further effects of the situation on mind and body. The *Reed Triggerplant*, positively chosen, indicates the person is aware of the accumulative effect of the trauma of the situation on their feelings of vitality. This flower indicates that the situation and ones very much like it, have been occurring constantly for a long period of time. The *Cowkicks*, positively chosen, also indicates a vitality problem that the person acknowledges, and comes from the shattering effect the situation has on them. The person is finding it hard to piece themselves together and keep going. The *West Australian Smokebush*, positively

31

chosen, adds to this scenario. Here too, the effects of the situation are being experienced in a way the person is very aware of, such as a feeling of vagueness, of not being able to keep focused, or perhaps feeling light headed. These effects may lead to some anxiety and feeling that the person is losing their grip.

Some Problems Solved

Problem: the person has chosen a great many flowers

Solution: the problem is that you have a general diagnosis not a specific one. The person is thinking about many areas of their life and the complexities are showing in their selection. To avoid this happening always be sure the person has one brick wall, one problem, they are concentrating on before they start selecting.

If you haven't done this and the selection of flowers has been too many, you can at this point correct the diagnosis. The person can now concentrate on the problem/situation most needed to be worked on and choose, from the first selection, the seven most strongly impacting flowers. (these can be either negatively impacting or positively impacting)

Problem: the person doesn't want to disclose their problem at the beginning of the diagnosis.

Solution: this is not a problem, both the Flower Affinity Diagnosis and Baihui Diagnosis can be done with the therapist not knowing the specific problem. They must be sure, however that the person is clear in their own mind about their problem, or the diagnosis will not be decisive.

During, and because of, the choice of flowers in the diagnosis, all is revealed to the therapist without the person having to talk about it, and sometimes this is very comforting for those traumatized by events in their life. The flowers are sure to comfort the person and help them to open up for future sessions.

GROUPING BY COLOUR

An extra step to the Flower Affinity Diagnosis can be the grouping into colours of the flowers. This is particularly interesting and useful when one or two colours predominate in a person's selection.

The flowers when grouped by colour show one particular aspect of their healing nature that the colour represents. The flower has mastery over this colour with both the ability to balance it by releasing an excess of the mind state that the colour represents, or building up to a positive balance when there is a deficiency of this colour. In the case of the complementary colours of Red/Green or Blue/Yellow the flower has a mastery over the aspect of mind that the combined colours deal with.

Ideally a person has a healthy and positive balance of all the colours representing their different attributes. A problem situation will often accentuate any imbalances occurring.

The following chart is a simple guide for those interested in this way of grouping and viewing flower choices.

Colour	In Positive Balance	Excessive	Deficient
Yellow	carefree, bright, alert unsettled	scattered, shallow, glum	sad, dull,
Blue	focussed, calm, consistent	constrictive, pessimistic,	unfocussed, rigid, erratic
Red	vitality, courage, strength	aggressive, insensitive, danger	weak lethargic, fearful
Green	nurturing, freeing, peaceful	insipid, weak, indulgent	restless, frenetic
Pink	discrimination, inner strength, sensitivity	over sensitive, emotional	uncentred, influenced
Violet Purple	open, loving nature	demanding, self centred	unfeeling, hard
Orange	caring detachment, objectivity	cut off, intellectually justifying	irrational, biased
White	purity, enlightening, higher perspective	clinical, remote	lack of vision and higher aspirations
Brown	neutralizing, grounded, balanced, practical	limited vision earth bound	ungrounded, unconnected, impractical

Black is not a colour, but an absence of colour. It indicates that caution should be taken due to the powerful forces of transformation at work, like death.

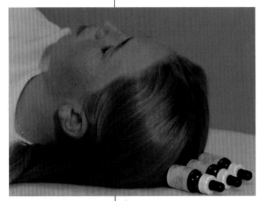

3,   *BAIHUI DIAGNOSIS*

The word Baihui comes from China and literally means "hundred meetings". It is the name given to the acu-point at the top of the head on the governing meridian, or Du channel. This acu-point is considered the governing point for all meridians and acu-points, and through this point all organs, tissue, glands and associated mind states can be accessed.

Many years ago we used this point as a diagnostic and interactive treatment point without knowing the ancient Qi Kung science behind it. We did however know about the Sahasrara Chakra which lay at a conceptual point just above the head where all mind states are mastered and governed.

This Chakra is called the thousand petalled lotus, the symbolic petals of which represent the thousand mental propensities, or mind states, that humans express. In Yogic science there are seven major Chakras, the first six are the doors through which the fifty basic "Vrttis", or mind states, are expressed. These are then multiplied by two, due to the fact they can be both internally and externally expressed. This then gives one hundred possibilities of mind expression. This hundred is then further multiplied by the 5 motor and 5 sensory organs associated with each Chakra. These sense and motor organs are:

sense of smell, of taste, of sight, of touch, of hearing and the motor organs of excretion, sexuality, feet, hands and voice. The multiplication by these ten brings the final number of expressions for the mind to one thousand.

By using the adjacent point on the head to the Sahasrara Chakra we were able to see the interaction of a flower essence with the state of mind dominant in the person being diagnosed or treated. The way, given thousands of years ago, to locate this point was by the measurement of placing the patient's four fingers tightly side by side, starting from the middle between the eye brows, moving backwards three times, which ends at the point at the top and back of the head.

We found that even the flower essences in their bottles placed on this point would interact with it and produce diagnostic effects in the patient. Then in 1990 during our study of acupuncture we discovered the existence of the Chinese Qi Kung's Baihui point. The ancient Chinese located this point by making a line from the bottom of the ear lobe to the top-middle of the ear and extending this line to the mid point on the top of the head. Lo and behold it is exactly the same point as the Sahasrara point.

We knew from our decades of study of Yogic science that the sciences of ancient times had all come from sources in Northern India and the Himalayas and spread down through India and China to the rest of Asia and the orient. This was another proof of their common origins. The different cultures developed the sciences, according to their preferences, into various arts. India was more a seat for extension and understanding of the mind and consciousness, with the science of the Chakras, Yoga, meditation practices, homeopathy and Aryuveda, and China delved more into the elements and primal forces, with the science of Qi Kung, herbal medicines, acu-puncture and the martial art, Kung Fu.

So between them, the Baihui point and the Sahasrara corresponding point, accessed all the organs, all the meridians, all the acu-points, all the Chakras, all the Vrttis, all the glands and all the collective mental states associated with each.

We decided to develop a set method to use this point as diagnosis and called it Baihui Diagnosis. We found that a person could self diagnose accurately through our new method, often helped by a therapist as facilitator only. The person wanting diagnosis would access all the thought forms of their problem or situation and flower essences would be tested on the Baihui point to see the interaction and healing effect. This method of diagnosis is very accurate and enlightening for both patient and therapist. However it needs to be conducted properly to achieve these results. The steps are as follows:-

STEPS OF THE BAIHUI DIAGNOSIS

1. The place to conduct the Baihui diagnosis must be quiet and there should be no interruptions for at least half an hour.

2. The person should get in touch with the area of their life and their being that they want diagnosed with essences. If a therapist is conducting the diagnosis then they should talk to the patient until they are sure the person is in contact with a real problem and not just an intellectual idea about it. The interaction and diagnosis is most clear when the person is in touch with the state of mind for which they have sought healing.

3. The person being diagnosed should be lying down comfortably on their back. (It is best not to use a bed if you are self diagnosing at home because the associations with sleep may hamper your concentration) A white or neutral coloured pillow or towel is then placed under the head and the hair arranged so as to allow access to the Baihui point.

4. The person then activates their problem/thought form, by getting in touch with the feelings and atmospheres associated with it. As with the Flower Affinity Diagnosis the person may find the easiest way to access the feelings is to replay in their mind situations from the past that typify the problem.

5. When the person knows the feelings are activated, the diagnosis begins. If the person has chosen flowers in the Flower Affinity Diagnosis, the flower they chose and rated first, because it evoked the strongest response, is placed on the Baihui point, the bottle base touching the scalp. If there has not been Flower Affinity Diagnosis the person or therapist will use an essence they have chosen from looking at the psychological profile of the person's problem and matching it with a flower's healing properties.

6. At no time should the person facilitating a diagnosis ask leading questions or give any hint of what the reaction to a flower essence should be. Objectivity is essential for an accurate diagnosis. The therapist should only listen to reports of any changes taking place, asking sometimes when the patient is quiet, "could you tell me what is happening now?"

7. After a few minutes with the first essence, the patient reports as to any changes. If there are no changes, continue, but first be sure the person is still concentrating on the problem they wanted to work with.

8. If there are changes, or reactions, this shows that this essence is producing a healing interaction. As the interaction gets to a plateau phase and no further changes are occurring, then the next essence is placed to the left or right of the first one, the base of the bottle touching the scalp as before.

We strongly advise the use of the Flower Affinity Diagnosis before the Baihui Diagnosis for the following reasons:

a) People can have difficulties being open and therefore vulnerable with their problems to a therapist. The real issue may then be avoided if you are relying only on verbal cues.

b) People can be unaware of the subconscious base to their issues.

c) There can be communication problems between the person being diagnosed and the therapist. This can be because of different ways of expressing, language difficulties, or problems coming to a common reference point in understanding.

d) In Flower Affinity Diagnosis people are choosing their own pathway to being healed, and we feel this is an optimum path for the healing process.

9. When the Flower Affinity Diagnosis has not been used before the Baihui diagnosis, the following may occur. After seven minutes or so, there may have been no changes at all with the first flower essence on the Baihui point. It is likely that it was not an appropriate choice, and does not relate to the problem. As such it can be removed. However, if the person has not been "feeling" the problem and atmosphere from the beginning, this lack of reaction will also occur, hence the importance of the first steps in this diagnostic technique.

NOTE: all flowers chosen, (top 7 selected), in a Flower Affinity Diagnosis, should be left on the Baihui point in sequence through to the completion of diagnosis. (See point no.10). The combination of the flowers chosen will produce the total effect.

10. With the second essence, as with the first, the person reports on any changes, and as these reactions plateau, another essence is placed next to the others, always touching the scalp, whether to the side, or stacked one on another in a pyramid shape.

11. At any time, even after the first essence, the Baihui Diagnosis may be complete. It is complete when the person reports a complete change which is expressed in one of three ways.

a) They can no longer evoke the problem or atmospheres in their mind.

b) They sense a whole new attitude and perspective towards the problem, which comes as a revelation.

c) They feel relieved and at peace, or perhaps joyous and inspired.

So, whenever these states occur, the Baihui is complete and the flowers that have created the healing effect are then noted for making an oral prescription.

If you have done the Flower Affinity Diagnosis before the Baihui, you usually have seven flowers, in order from one to seven, to work with in the Baihui Diagnosis. Note that the Baihui can be complete at any time between the first or the last essence. What this means is, that although relevant to the healing issues, the essences that were not needed to complete the diagnosis are not essential for healing the central issues and states of mind. These central states, often gave birth to other issues, and as they are healed the other issues disappear. Any flowers pertaining to these "extra" issues are therefore no longer needed.

If we take an example from the Flower Affinity Diagnosis section, the person may have concluded their Baihui Diagnosis before the essences for vitality were added. In other words, once they have healed the pain and regained their self esteem, their vitality automatically improved.

Some Problems Solved

Problem: the person can't concentrate from the very beginning.

Solution: use the *Pink Trumpet Flower* on the Baihui Point while they get into the feelings involved and leave it there, on the Baihui point, throughout the diagnosis. It will not, however be part of the oral prescription.

Problem: the person talks a lot during the Baihui and gets involved in other issues.

Solution: gently and repeatedly remind the person to stay with the original thought form and feelings, to work with the same scenario replaying in their mind.

Problem: the person intellectualizes the changes they are experiencing and loses touch with their feelings.

Solution: don't engage in conversation, gently keep the person focused on the original problem and, as at the beginning, steer them back to being in touch with the atmosphere of it.

Problem: everything seems to suddenly stop, or go "cold", yet the problem is still there.

Solution: the person has probably reached a deeper level of their mind, perhaps it is uncomfortable. Add one or more of these essences that match the reason for the pause or intensity; *Menzies Banksia, Illyarrie, Ribbon Pea, Macrozamia*, to the essences already there, so the mind will keep progressing through the diagnosis.

Menzies Banksia heals the fear of pain being repeated.

Illyarrie heals the fear of suppressed memories.

Ribbon Pea heals irrational fears of death or annihilation.

Macrozamia heals painful memories to do with sexual trauma.

Each of these essences will help the person through to the next stage of the diagnosis when matched correctly. Whichever of these were used can be added to the oral prescription at the end of the diagnosis.

Problem: the person is experiencing a deep well of emotions, is crying, anxious or angry.

Solution: definitely the right essences are being used, but the mind is not continuing with the healing journey and is getting side tracked. *Dampiera* is added to the diagnosis to allow a releasing of the emotion so the rest of the diagnosis will proceed. It can be added to the prescription at the end of the diagnosis.

It is also good to consider if the *Menzies Banksia, Illyarrie, Ribbon Pea, or Macrozamia*, might be needed.

Problem: the Baihui seems complete but the person wonders "where to go to from here?".

Solution: the *Star of Bethlehem* (Australian) is added to the diagnosis. This essence opens the mind to creative solutions and options for the way ahead. It gives a final touch to the diagnosis and can be used in the prescription afterwards.

4.   *FLORAL ACU-POINTS*

As diagnostic tools, floral acu-points and their specific flower essences can be utilized in three ways.

1.   **By Physical Symptom**

A person having a particular physical problem can match this to the *physical symptom* list (an alphabetical index at the back of the book). In this list a particular acu-point is given for a common physical problem, and one or two flower essences which are used on this acu-point. The person then selects the flower for which the *Psychological profile* matches the problem, and this is applied on the acu-point. (see floral acu-point application section)

2.   **By Psychological Profile**

A person whose problem matches the *Psychological profile* of a particular flower, chooses the acu-point which is specific for that flower essence and then applies it to the acu-point.

3.   **By Ah-shi Point Reaction**

A person gently, but firmly, presses a cotton bud on the different acu-points of the ears, both left and right. Any acu-points that are tender or sore indicate a need for rebalancing of that organ, or area of the body. These tender spots are called Ah-shi points (meaning "ah, yes!" in Chinese). The person then looks up the flower essences that pertain to this point, selects the *Psychological profile* which matched the mind state/problem they have, and then applies this flower essence to the point.

To have a wide range of application techniques for flower essences enhances their use. Matching the needs, comfort of use and life style limitations, of the person taking the flower essences, can also be vital to the therapy being undertaken thoroughly until the healing process is complete. If there is some problem with remembering regular oral doses, then a floral acu-point or bath therapy could be used. This is better than someone struggling and perhaps giving up on their treatment before they have the full benefit of the flower essences they chose or were prescribed. In some cases it may be difficult for a person to do the floral acu-point therapy themselves and so the oral doses, baths or sprays can be more helpful.

Ideally, to get to the core issues and heal them thoroughly, oral doses are taken. This can be whole or part of the treatment, in some cases the last phase of the therapy.

1. ORAL DOSES

How Many Drops Makes an Oral Dose?

The wildflower essences work between the higher aspects of the mind and the fundamental aspects of the body. With oral dosing the amount of the flower essence used can be adjusted to the level of activity upon which the mind state is most obviously manifesting. This can enhance the rate of response. The more essence used, the denser the level of activity, i.e. the more physical, and the less essence used, the more subtle the level. As a general guide, 70 drops per 25ml is a maximum (physical level) and 3 drops per 25ml the minimum (mind and finer levels). Between these levels is a sliding scale within which an estimation of where the mind state is impacting is made, and from this, therefore, how much essence will be needed in making up an oral dose.

The following is an example.

Person A : Problem/situation; very bad acne, self conscious about the way he or she looks.
Wildflower Essence diagnosed; Hybrid Pink Fairy Orchid dosage level 70 drops

Person B: Problem/situation; very shy, blushes easily, can't look others in the eye.
Wildflower Essence diagnosed; Hybrid Pink Fairy Orchid dosage level 40 drops

Person C: Problem/situation; finds it difficult to talk to groups of people, is unnerved, wondering if others are liking or accepting them.
Wildflower Essence diagnosed; Hybrid Pink Fairy Orchid dosage level 20 drops

Person D: Problem/situation; wants to be able to maintain their own mind state and humour wherever they are and whoever they are with.

Wildflower Essence diagnosed; Hybrid Pink Fairy Orchid dosage level 10 drops

Person E: Problem/situation; wishes to be able to be highly intuitive of people and Life, yet maintain internal integrity and peace.

Wildflower Essence diagnosed; Hybrid Pink Fairy Orchid dosage level 3 drops

The example describes some general degrees in impact from the physical to the subtle mind. Ascertaining which level to work with, is made for each flower essence individually. This means that if there are 5 or more essences chosen or prescribed then each one is evaluated as to the area/level of impact which it will address.

If the Flower Affinity Diagnosis has been the diagnostic technique used, then the person being diagnosed can be asked if they have any physical reaction when they are in the midst of their problem/situation. This can give a guide as to the different levels for each flower for the dosage.

If the Baihui diagnosis has been the diagnostic technique used, then the person will have often experienced different physical states during the diagnosis and these can be a guide.

For example, a person feels a tightness in their belly when remembering something which evokes feelings of anger. During a Baihui to diagnose flower essences for that state of mind, the person may again feel the tightness, or discomfort in their belly. When a certain flower essence, like perhaps the Black Kangaroo Paw is placed on the Baihui, the feeling gradually disappears. This indicates that the Black Kangaroo Paw heals the mind-state that then manifests in the body as discomfort. The number of drops in the dilution will then be in the high range.

The most relevant aspect is to remember that the more precise one is with choosing the level of activity, and matching the flower essence dosage, the more the healing is enhanced and expedited.

Preparation of Dosage

After assessing how many drops of each flower are needed, they are put into a dropper bottle with one of the following preserving liquids as a base; brandy, vodka, cider vinegar, malt vinegar, or vegetable glycerin. Brandy can be diluted by quarter or half with spring water (or a pure water source). Essences can also be mixed into pure water only, however they must be kept refrigerated and full potency will only last a few days.

The steps are as follows:

1. Put a small amount of the preserving liquid into the bottle (one that has a dropper).

2. Put the amount of drops in for each flower selected.

3. Fill the bottle up to the shoulder level (i.e. in a 25ml bottle, up to the 25ml mark, not up to the top)

4. Succuss the mixture. This means to put the top on securely and pound the base of the bottle on your palm for ten seconds. This is a method of integrating the preserving medium with the subtle flower essences properties.

The mixture is now ready to be taken.

Taking the Dosage

There are two methods of taking the oral dose.

1. The flower essence can be taken, one drop under the tongue six times over the day.
   or

2. The flower essence can be taken six drops in a half glass of water, morning and late afternoon/evening.

The oral dose (in a 25ml bottle) will last between 6 to 8 weeks. At the end of this period the person can assess how deeply the healing has gone within, and whether it will be continued for another 6 to 8 weeks to ensure completion.

There are combinations of wildflower essences already made up for use. These include:

1. the Wildflower Relief Elixir: a general restorative for times of stress and trauma.

2. The 21st Century Survival Kit Essences which include combinations for:
   Inner Strength, Positivity, Creativity, Emotions in Balance, Relaxation. Energy, Concentration and Meditation.

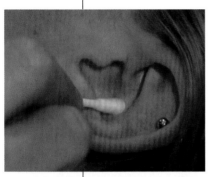

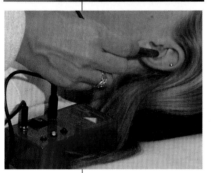

2. FLORAL ACU-POINTS, FLORAL ACU-PRESSURE and FLOWER ESSENCE PROJECTOR

It may be asked, "Why use flower essences on acu-points?".

The meridian channels of Qi Kung science, (used in acupuncture therapy), are pathways for the Qi or vital force. These meridians cover the body , like a network, and link all the organs and body areas. Each channel has acu-points which access the meridian at different places. These acu-points are like doorways into the meridian.

The meridian pathways and the acu-point doorways each have specific qualities which align them with specific flower essences. When there is overactive or underactive vital force in a particular organ or meridian, a flower essence that matches the qualities of that particular organ or meridian can restore the balance. The messages that the flower essences hold, when aligned to the correct acu-point and meridian are excellent for transforming states of physical health and consciousness.

We have found that combining specific flower essences with acu-points greatly speeds the healing outcomes and is particularly useful when a person is suffering from acute states of mind and body.

For this book we have chosen mainly the ear acu-points which are easy to locate and use, and a few points on the head and body. The ear has a complete energetic map of the body on it, like our hands and feet, and so can be utilized to access all meridians and body organs and areas.

After selection of the correct flower essence for use on a specific floral acu-point, (see diagnostic technique section - floral acu-points) there a four methods by which the flower essence can be applied.

1. Applying Direct to the Point

By simple application of a few drops of the flower essence. This is mainly used on points such as the Baihui acu-point, the extra six point, the navel point and the Heart 1 point in the middle of the underarm. The points are treated a minimum of twice daily and sometimes hourly (each flower's section will describe this).

2. **Floral Acu-pressure**

    By applying a few drops of the flower essence to a cotton bud and pulsing on the point for five minutes. This is used on most points. When using this point on the ear or body, both ears or both sides of the body are used. Usual treatments are twice a day for a number of weeks.

3. **Flower Essence Projector**

    The Flower Essence Projector has been designed so as to enhance and not to disturb the healing qualities of the flower essences. The word "projector" has been used to describe the effect of projecting the flower essence into the Qi flow of the body. The process can be understood in this way. All flower essences have a vital force component and a consciousness component. The consciousness component is like an idea or concept. When you occupy your mind with the concept of enjoying achieving a cherished goal, the stamina and willpower to carry it out is like the vital force needed to manifest it. So integrating the flower essences into acu-points is like integrating vitality and consciousness, linking the flower essence into the vital flows that already exist in the person.

    To apply the flower essence with a 100 percent result would mean the flower essence was 100 percent absorbed into the Qi flow. Unfortunately when using acu-pressure with the pulsing technique there is some natural resistance which affects the full healing potential. We found using the projector greatly reduces the resistance to integration of the flower essence with vital force.

    The Flower Essence Projector is used by first applying a few drops of flower essence to the matching acu-point on the ear, (both ears). The acu-point is now covered in the specifically matched flower essence and the light source is placed on it for about five minutes.

4. **Acupuncture (for qualified acupuncturists only)**

    To apply, dip the acupuncture needles in the flower essence before needling the matching acu-point. (NOTE: the use of Menzies Banksia on the acu-point before needling greatly reduces any experience of pain. Dampiera can be used where the body grips the needles tightly, making withdrawal difficult.)

3. TOPICAL APPLICATION

(For direct application and Body Work, Massage, Chiropractic/Osteopathy, Physiotherapy etc.)

Some of the wildflower essences are effective in a simple topical application. This means that they can be used directly to a body area from the bottle concentrate, or a dilution of this. The dilution can be one part flower essence and two parts brandy and the brandy can already be diluted by quarter or half with spring water (or a pure water source). The mixture is then succussed. This means to put the top on securely and pound the base of the bottle on your palm for ten seconds. (note: this dilution is only suitable for topical application)

WILDFLOWERS COMMONLY USED

The wildflower essences for pain responses in the body:

All essences are reapplied as needed. For chronic problems, regular applications, three times a day are suggested.

Menzies Banksia: this essence is applied to points on the body radiating the pain message, a pain hot spot or trigger point. It is also applied around (not on) a painful wound or surgery site.

Dampiera: for any pain resulting in tightening of muscles, cramping or spasming this essence is applied to the body area.

Macrozamia: for any pain that is accompanied by the blocking , or production of, fluid in the body (like swelling). This essence is applied to the body area. It is also applied around around wounds or surgery sites.

Purple Flag Flower: for any pain that is caused by pressure build up, or stressed tissue, this essence is applied to the body area.

Wildflower essences for problems of blocked or erratic nerve messages in the body (which can also produce painful responses):

Ursinia and Leafless Orchid: for lack of body response, erratic or uncontrollable responses, tremors and shakes. The essences are applied along the line of the lack of, or erratic response, and, if possible from the area following a pathway to the adjacent spinal area. For example, if the hand has the problem, the essences are used on this area and up the arm to the shoulder and spine.

Wildflower essence for problems of fainting, recovery from anaesthesia:

West Australian Smokebush: for fainting, recovery from anaesthesia, trauma and shock. This essence can be applied to the Extra six acu-point (see acu-point section) and/or applied to the forehead regularly, from temple to temple.

Using this essence to recover quickly from anaesthetic greatly enhances speed of healing and regeneration, especially after long and difficult operations.

Wildflower essence for problems of energy drain:

Leafless Orchid: for energy problems, particularly when convalescing,or recovering from a great expenditure of energy, especially when it has been expended on other people. This essence is applied a few drops at a time to the Baihui acu-point on the top of the head (see acu-point section), every fifteen minutes or half an hour.

Wildflower essences for problems of nausea:

Rose Cone Flower: for problems of nausea, including morning sickness, reaction to drugs etc. Applied regularly to the navel a few drops at a time.

Hybrid Pink Fairy Orchid: also used with Rose Cone Flower for morning sickness. Apply a few drops regularly to the navel.

Black Kangaroo Paw: also used with Rose Cone Flower for morning sickness and general nausea caused by toxicity (like reaction to drugs or bad food). Apply a few drops regularly to the navel.

Wildflower essence for problems of sleeplessness:

Hops Bush: for feelings of speediness, being unable to relax and wind down, restless or difficult sleeping habits. Applied along midline of scalp to the back of the head hourly from 4pm to bedtime. An oral dose of Hops Bush, 6 drops in a half glass of water, taken at four and six o'clock in the afternoon, is also suggested.

Wildflower essence for problems of worrying during convalescence and recovery:

Golden Waitsia: for overreaction to little or prolonged discomforts, fussing over unessential areas of health. Apply to soles of the feet twice daily.

Creams and Lotions

Combinations of wildflower essences have been suspended in creams and lotions for ease of use. There is a Pain cream and the Great Reliever body lotion which are used for: general pain, cramping, spasm, bruising, burns, insect bites, damaged tissue, tonifying, circulation and sports preparation (to avoid injury and stiffness). The second combination is Stress Reliever Skin Lustre cream and Stress Reliever body lotion which are used for general stress, tension, sleeplessness, and some side effects of these situations like tight chest and constricted breathing.

4. BATHS

All the wildflower essences can be used in baths, both full body and foot baths. Today many people have access to spa baths also. The motion of spa baths has an enhancing effect for this therapy, with the continual linking and integrating of the subtle flower essence qualities into the water as they surge around and against the body.

Any selection of the wildflower essences can be made to match the mind states needing healing. However the more careful the selection, and the more it pertains to one particular healing effect, the better. It is wise to avoid using too many essences at once and possibly blurring the effect of the ones that are most needed.

For a full body size bath or spa, twenty drops of flower essence (in total) are added to the bath, under the tap, from the time the bath is half full. This means, for example, that if you are using five flowers you will use four drops of each essence.

Ideally the first fifteen minutes of soaking in the bath will be without anything else being added to the bath. It is also suggested to keep as submerged as possible to allow the whole body to be surrounded by the essences.

For a foot bath or baby bath, ten drops in total are added to the water.

There are some wildflower essence combinations which have particular therapeutic benefits.

General Stress: this combination helps to release tension and mind states that hold on to stress.

Golden Waitsia, Hops Bush, Purple Flag Flower, Hybrid Pink Fairy Orchid.

Children: helping maintain calm and composure. Helping the child to keep an overall perspective on their life while learning to integrate the different aspects. To help with centering themselves and not becoming overwrought by all the events and experiences of the day.

White Nymph Waterlily, Leafless Orchid.

Babies: to keep them in touch with the soft benevolent Love underlying all Life, regardless of all the difficult daily adjustments they are making. To promote free mind states which don't get caught in set patterns, like having to wake up, or cry repeatedly out of habit rather than need.

Purple Nymph Waterlily, Blue China Orchid.

Couples: to bring out the Love nature from a deep level, and promote the desire to see the happiness of your partner. To regain spontaneity and carefreeness, releasing the need to focus on petty aspects of the relationship. To experience the bliss of tenderness and the merging of Souls.

Purple Nymph Waterlily, Golden Waitsia, Red Leschenaultia.

General feelings of sadness or anxiety: these essences promote a lightness of being, enabling the person to get in touch with the positive and balanced perspective on Life. It inspires a sense of being grounded and at ease.

Yellow Flag Flower, Brown Boronia, Hybrid Pink Fairy Orchid.

General Energy Combination: to help restore connections to vital force, Qi, to regulate that Qi, and promote mind states that keep healthy balance of focus.

Pink Fountain Triggerplant, Purple Enamel Orchid, Rabbit Orchid, Pink Trumpet Flower.

5.   SPRAYS

Wildflower essences can be used as a spray therapy, both around a person and in areas where people spend their time.

A clean, new, spray bottle is used, and can be of any size. To make up a mixture add a little pure or spring water to the spray bottle, then add a total of 20 drops of a flower essence or essences per 250mls of water. The mixture is then succussed. This means to put the top on securely and pound the base of the bottle on your palm for ten seconds.

The person or area is sprayed around and over, for about 15 seconds. This can be done daily to build up a healing effect.

The following are some wildflower combinations used for common healing needs:-

Bed Spray: to be able to rest peacefully and let go of any frenetic energy. To keep a focus of positivity and optimism, ready for a new day and open to experiences.

Hops Bush, Yellow Flag Flower, Dampiera.

Study/Work Chair Spray: to be open to learning and to see the purpose for learning. Not to get caught up too much in the small details and lose sight of the overall importance. To move the mind away from fixations on problems and concepts, and be able to come back to them when the mind is refreshed. Not to divert the mind away from the task. Not to feel split in the desire to either sit down to work, or to go off and play. To keep direction and motivation in balance with the needs to keep refreshed.

Yellow Leschenaultia, Golden Waitsia, Brown Boronia, Pink Trumpet, Red Beak Orchid.

Family Room Spray: to help the balance of the masculine and feminine aspects. To bring orientation towards collective welfare while individual desires are achieved. To promote depth and understanding in relationships, and not to overreact to emotional upsets.

Macrozamia, Balga, Rabbit Orchid, Purple Eremophila,
Mauve Melaleuca.

Personal Spray: for cleansing the etheric body, keeping the mind free from the accumulation of negative influences and maintaining inner integrity. Also helpful to maintain inner resilience against illnesses and viruses.

Shy Blue Orchid, Antiseptic Bush, Geraldton Wax.

6. MEDITATIONS

The effects of the resonance of a wildflower can be enhanced by getting in touch with the flower via a visualization-meditation technique.

You may select a wildflower, the properties of which you particularly need that day, or qualities of a wildflower that you are working towards as part of your healing journey.

It is best to practice the meditation in a quiet place where you will not be disturbed, making sure you are comfortable in a seated position. Look closely at the photograph of the flower, getting a clear image of it in your mind. Read the meditation poem for that flower many times until the rhythm of its message settles in your mind.

Next, close your eyes and imagine yourself very small and placed in the middle of the flower, looking out through your eyes at its petals. See yourself with the problems you are facing, or situations in your Life, sitting in the flower.

Allow yourself time to be with the image of the flower in this way. Observe the journey your mind makes and relax into the healing atmosphere.

Another way you can tap into Mother Nature's rich storehouse of healing is to access directly the healing from your garden or out in a park or nature reserve. You can do the meditation technique sitting right by any flower which has a strong impact on your mind. The flower which you choose is going to be interacting with you and, like a dear friend sitting next to you, will benefit you by just being there.

Often after doing the meditation on a flower, a renewed appreciation of the floral kingdom comes, and we realize that we are surrounded by so many freely given healing gifts.

One of the greatest testaments as to the effectiveness of the wildflowers in healing comes from the animal kingdom. The healing attributes of the wildflowers impact on wild and domestic animals in the same way as they do with humans. In fact due to the nature of animal consciousness, there are perhaps far fewer barriers to transformation and healing than with humans.

Our experience has shown us that animals are very eager to follow a healing path and do not resist the gentle advances of the flowers being administered to them.

Whether it was for physical problems, like pain, or states of mind, like aggression the results have always been excellent and particularly rewarding.

Some people would argue that animals don't have a mind, or a soul for that matter. In fact many humans show everyday their lack of appreciation of the finer attributes of animals, even the ones they say they are attached to and love like a family member. Somehow, because animals don't speak their mind verbally, human beings don't analyze what their effect on an animal is. Perhaps when many humans find it difficult to understand and properly respond to the non-speaking (including babies and young children), deaf or blind members of their own species, it is little wonder they take great liberties with the animal species they dominate.

Domestic Animals

With domestic animals, the problems needing healing often arise from: (1.) a lack of understanding of their physical needs and individual bearing and (2.) a lack of proper treatment and response from the humans around them. This does not mean they can't be healed of their problem, but the extent of the healing will depend on some realizations of the owners. For example, flower essence therapy will not be a permanent solution for an aggressive dog whose owner has a habit of beating him. However, if a dog is aggressive from a previous owner and the new owner is kind, then the dog can be healed of its past experiences.

An individual animal can also have particular sensitivities and reactions to its environment which may be exaggerated. An owner may not be aware how this all came about, but still the animal can be helped. Many mind states in animals lead to their physical states, as with humans. Physical symptoms are the body's way of trying to express and change the way things are until a healthful balance is achieved.

Some problems are particular to the mind-set of a species. Flower essences for any weaknesses of that mind-set greatly enhance the animal's life. Horses* are a vegetarian animal, which means it is prey for other animals,

as part of the "Equine Welfare" programme, the Academy has conducted special research with horses.

and built for defense from attack. Mother Nature has given them a sensitive disposition, which when under extreme physical pain will easily let go of their physical body and end the distress.

When horses get extreme colic one must act swiftly before the death-release response occurs. The standard wildflowers used for colic, topically on their bellies, are Menzies Banksia, and on the spine and above the tail, Ursinia. Menzies Banksia breaks up the fear that the pain will keep being repeated, and through this message, also breaks up the intensity of the pain and the fear which, in the extreme, will produce death. Ursinia realigns areas into a healthy synthesis. It reactivates the connections in the functions of the different parts of the intestine. All this healing can usually be achieved before the vet arrives. The animals will respond exactly as a human would do, become relieved and start reviving.

Wild Animals

* the Academy runs a "Roo Rescue Programme", which provides mothers for orphans and a free service of consultations and wildflower essences for wildlife rescue groups.

Some of the most deeply satisfying work we have done with animals has been in the saving of wildlife*, often in physical trouble due to the influence of human civilization. This work has been also ratifying the healing definitions of the essences, as the work with domestic animals has done.

The first time we lived with a pair of orphan kangaroo babies, called Joeys, we learnt a lot about the ways animal and human masculinity and femininity mirrored each other. The male, Rajah, was completely dependent on the care of the little female, Radha. She preened and cleaned him, and he would run to her to embrace whenever a noise frightened him. They would stand hugging in the middle of the living room, watching/listening to the television. Rajah also perpetually sucked his thumb, whether standing or in his pouch. He even developed a way to rest his elbow in his other hand so his sucking arm wouldn't get tired.

We were a bit concerned as to how he would fare amongst the other males when going to the half way house before release into the wild. Being a male meant he would have to take his place in the mob, in the hierarchy of the rough and tumble bachelor parties. We started him on Balga (Blackboy wildflower essence) to help him mature his masculine strength into a balance.

Then one day a friend suggested trying him out with her male of the same age, Rhubarb, who was supremely confident. Rhubarb came over in his pouch, and immediately upon seeing him, the female sensed he was a good catch. She followed him around, and Rajah at first watched, trying to take the whole new series of events in. Then he made his move.

In a stance we had never seen him in, he raised himself up to twice his height towering over Rhubarb who started to object but quickly thought better of it. Very quickly Rhubarb bowed down with arms on the floor before him and made supplicatory coughing sounds. We knew Rajah was going to be fine in the wild, and he was.

Often the most important work of the essences is with countering the shock and trauma, both physically and mentally, that animals have with injury, being thrust suddenly into human hands, or being orphaned. The results have been very satisfying and inspiring. In most cases the essences have been used externally on the animals' bodies.

For physical problems the same symptoms as humans experience apply, so for pain, use the essences for pain, for energy loss the same, and so on. Topical applications are also used in the same way.

Some common treatments for mind states in both domestic and wild animals are as follows:-

Red Leschenaultia and Orange Spiked Pea: exaggerated, aggressive, attacking reactions.

Ribbon Pea, Hops Bush and Fuchsia Gum: fearfulness and nervous overreaction.

Purple Nymph Waterlily and Southern Cross: inability to maintain equipoise.

Macrozamia and Goddess Grasstree: lack of feminine or maternal response.

Macrozamia and Balga: lack of, or extremes of, masculine response.

Hybrid Pink Fairy Orchid and Geraldton Wax: overreaction, sensitivity to environment, inability to cope with new circumstances.

Goddess Grasstree and Purple Nymph Waterlily: for the trauma of being orphaned, not to give up and die.

Pink Fountain Triggerplant and Cowkicks: for lack of connection to vitality and life force, inability to revive strength.

Blue China Orchid and Brown Boronia: caught in unnecessary repetitive and/or destructive behaviour patterns.

Ways to Administer the flower essences.

1. applied to the top of the animal's head six times over the day.
2. given in the bottle feeder or water bowl, 1 drop per ten millilitres.
3. given in fruit, where appropriate to the animals diet, for adults, ten drops on a piece of fruit, once a day, for infants half the amount.

The Wildflowers from A to Z

Holding Aloft the Inner Light

Positive Qualities
Key Words:

integrity

sanctity

cleansing

alert

focus

Problem Target
Key Words:

compromising

influenced

distracted

helpless

The essence of staying true to one's journey and accepting into one's life only that which will sustain and support the inner nature. For cleansing oneself of negative influences in the environment or a build up over time of such influences within oneself. This essence helps a person to be amongst the different aspects of Life and maintain inner sanctity by continual internal focus, alertness and not compromising the treasures of Life.

Mind - Common Uses:

For the person easily dazzled by external attractions and frivolous enjoyments, being influenced to the detriment of their overall welfare. For those who leave themselves too open to influences.
For those who feel a sense of frustration and helplessness with their situation and feel increasingly unable to manage what they have got themselves into.
For a person who feels weighed down by, and find themselves absorbing a build up of psychic "junk" from the atmosphere, or from people in an environment they spend time in.

The healing inspires keeping internal integrity and being true to one's inner Light. The new brightness, and non compromising focus of the person's mind dispels the influences of negative diversions.

Physical - Common Uses:

Also used in daily room, bed or area spraying (10 drops per 125ml water, then succussion) and in etherically cleansing baths (20 drops per full sized bath).

Healing Pathway to the Soul

On our journey through life there can be an accumulation of influences and energies which eventually cloud and disorientate us from our higher goals and aspirations. We can leave ourselves vulnerable to negative experiences by not focusing on where we are going. In this way we invite a range of experiences which can lead us away from our goals. Keeping ourselves fresh and alert to where a path can lead, keeps us on course for building worthwhile and positive experiences.

Meditation Poem

Antiseptic Bush

Within the bright jewel of my mind

the purity of Light is shining.

I see clearly.

My inner Path leads me on

to the treasures of Life.

The Strength of the Creative Warrior

Positive Qualities Key Words:

maturity

assertiveness

balancing

creativity

Problem Target Key Words:

destructive

aggressive

insensitive

immaturity

For the maturing of the male principle or the man within. For both men and women, the promoting of positive creativity, assertiveness, goal setting and achieving, that also nurtures an awareness and appreciation of the needs of the environment and people. Helpful in balancing achievement with life sustaining qualities such as caring and community/family spirit.

Mind - Common Uses:

Used for women and men who find it hard to be forthright and assertive, or whose assertiveness is aggressive and overpowering. Both these indicate a lack of maturity and full development of the masculine strength within.

Commonly used for young boys and girls and adolescents who cannot integrate their new sexuality (the assertive/masculinity) into their being, and are either lacking in their masculine strength, or are out of balance, with the negative, dangerous and destructive side predominant.

Used also for people who cannot tap into their creativity, their ability to go into new territory and explore original and new horizons.

The healing matures the masculine aspect to become a creative and inclusive field of activity which can be both assertive and caring at the same time.

Physical - Common Uses:

Also oral doses (60 drops per 25ml brandy, see "oral dosing") in cases of general problems of loose bowel movements.

Used topically on the lower intestinal area for diarrhoea.

Mind - Floral Acu-pressure

Psychological profile:
independent, self willed, does as one pleases.
The Cardiac Orifice acu-point of the ear. (see Pg 251)

Psychological profile:
Sexually under confident, anxiety about one's sexual ability,
impotence due to psychological problems.
The Testis (Ovary) acu-point of the ear. (see Pg 268)

Psychological profile:
sexual frigidity, aversion to sexuality.
The Genitalia (External) acu-point of the ear. (see Pg 254)
(use with the Macrozamia flower essence)

Psychological profile:
mentally confident, overly focused on implementing one's ideas.
Insensitive and out of touch with one's environment and other people.
The Kidney acu-point of the ear. (see Pg 260)

Physical - Floral Acu-pressure

Physical symptoms:
nausea, vomiting.
The Cardiac Orifice acu-point of the ear. (see Pg 251)
(see also Start's Spider Orchid)

Physical symptoms:
Epididymitis, irregular menstruation.
The Testis (Ovary) acu-point of the ear. (see Pg 268)

Physical symptoms: impotency, sexual frigidity.
(use with the Macrozamia flower essence)
The Genitalia (External) acu-point of the ear. (see Pg 254)
(see also White Nymph and Purple Nymph Waterlily)

Physical symptoms:
tinnitis and impaired hearing.
The Kidney acu-point of the ear. (see Pg 260)
(see also Brown Boronia, Geraldton Wax, Yellow Leschenaultia).

Healing Pathway to the Soul

Within us the creative force blends with the receptive force. If we are to become whole then the two must be at one. Our creative force expresses the power to protect and love the created Universe and to be fearless on our journey forward. The aboriginal people see the Balga and its flower as the warrior standing with his spear watching over the tribe.

Meditation Poem

Balga

My Path goes forward

straight and true.

Along the way

the tender petals shall not be crushed

and the thorns cannot hinder me.

Love is my strength.

*Positive Qualities
Key Words:*

forgiveness

sensitivity

Love

positivity

**Problem Target
Key Words:**

anger

hatred

negativity

obsession

hurt

The Joy of Forgiveness

The essence of forgiveness and love. To bring back the Light and re-sensitize after resentment and heavy emotional traumas one can't seem to forget. This essence brings people back to their own hearts rather than staying in their resentful gut reactions, to go forward in their lives and leave their negativity behind.

Mind - Common Uses:

Helpful to reduce the trauma in relationship break-ups and grief/loss/anger and obsessive cycles. Also for issues of control as in the cases of parents or other authority figures, which then get re-enacted in later life.
To help release the need to boil over past or current problems with people.
For those who like to see the people who have hurt them suffer.

Negative emotions have a tendency to grow and take over the mind, and like falling down an expanding pit, the mind has a Herculean task to get out.

The healing allows the mind to free itself from the negative focus and to pursue positive avenues that will enhance the experience of Joy in their life.

Physical - Common Uses:

In getting rid of general build up of toxicity, 4 drops in fresh lemon juice and water with a small pinch of salt, a half hour before eating in the morning for one month. Thereafter oral doses for a further eight weeks.

Mind - Floral Acu-pressure

Psychological profile:
Feeling overburdened, one becomes aggressive and insensitive in the pursuit of solutions.
Diaphragm acu-point on the ear. (see Pg 252)

Physical - Floral Acu-pressure

Physical symptoms:
For general nausea and morning sickness used with Rose Cone Flower on the navel (a few drops of each essence no pressure pulsing needed).
Physical symptoms:
hiccups, jaundice.
Diaphragm acu-point on the ear. (see Pg 252)
(see also Woolly Banksia)

Healing Pathway to the Soul

Some of the hardest lessons we learn are the ones confronting us because of betrayal by a person we care about or are vulnerable to. It is a test of our ability to keep the greater vision of the purpose and higher goals of our Soul while facing the events our personality is grappling with. To bring in the Light and allow our Soul to lead the way heals the personality and reasserts our direction, freeing us from the darkness of negativity and hurtful deeds.

Acu Pt. Pg 267, 262

Meditation Poem

Black Kangaroo Paw

I am a part of all Life

watching it and within it also.

Buffeted by storms

I do not lose my way

I keep my eyes on the Light

and fly freely to Joy.

Positive Qualities
Key Words:

**Positive Qualities
Key Words:**

strengthen

Self control

Will

renewal

change

**Problem Target
Key Words:**

addicted

weak

overwhelmed

obsessive

The Elevation of the Will

To strengthen the Will and take back control of the Self. To realize the beauty of inner focus and consistency in establishing a fulfilling life. Habits are like old arm chairs, lumpy but familiar, and the person has to fight against their own old programming to be able to change to healthy new directions and experiences. This essence is helpful in inspiring changes by breaking the hold of old patterns of behaviour that erode the quality of life.

Mind - Common Uses:

Where the person has become habituated in patterns of living and behaviour which hamper development, happiness or relationships with others. This essence helps the metamorphosing of the mind to its new pathways by being positive about self control, discipline and direction. With the benefits of the new way of being and the feelings of freeing and focusing of the Will, the person is encouraged and inspired to go forward consistently.

For children who have become set in routine patterns, for example: waking during the night, crying or being destructive to get attention, immediately reacting when not getting their own way.

For people battling addictions or obsessive behaviour patterns.

The healing strengthens the Will to reclaim the role of master of the mind. From this comes the strength to focus on what one desires to change, and to change it.

Healing Pathway to the Soul

Any expansion of consciousness is brought about by effort. This effort requires focus, direction and forward movement. Old habits imprison us and impede our progress. They have power because they give a false sense of security. To have free will is to break through the feelings of unwillingness to give up old ways, and to be spontaneously working with Life.

Meditation Poem

Blue China Orchid

The heavy garments are discarded

one by one.

Like a butterfly

I leave the cocoon

and stretch out into the sky.

Everywhere Life is beckoning,

within I feel the thrill.

*Positive Qualities
Key Words:*

giving

sharing

open

free

generous

*Problem Target
Key Words:*

voracity

selfishness

covetous

hoarding

petty

The Joy of Giving

The essence that inspires generosity and the openness to share what we have with others on all levels. The opening of a window in the Soul that reveals the basic needs of fellow beings and then rekindles the desire to give with grace and benevolence. Also helps to de-energize an unhealthy need to have and keep hold of material possessions.

Mind - Common Uses:

For people who try to avoid having to give of themselves or be generous. Often they are puzzled as to why other people don't have loving feelings for them. For others relating to these people it seems that these people are always suspicious of motives and wondering what others want from them. When people get annoyed or start to reject them these unhelpful persons will seem not to understand why people are reacting to them in this way.
For the people who are too involved with the fleeting pleasures of material objects, hoarding, hiding and holding onto what they have. This is really a very sad state of being and brings no joy at all.
For those with petty attitudes concerning what they own.

The healing enables the person to expand the mind beyond the tight constricting material focus, to a benevolent, open and more carefree approach. People and their feelings then become more important than "things".

Physical - Common Uses:

Used in cases of belly ache.

Mind - Floral Acu-pressure

Psychological profile:
attitudes of "I'm alright, life is going fine for me", but indifference to, or not wanting to be bothered about, other people's dilemmas or hardships.
Stomach acu-point of the ear. (see Pg 267)
Psychological profile: possessive and/or avaricious due to insecurity/fear of being without.
Liver acu-point on the ear. (see Pg 261)

Physical - Floral Acu-pressure

Physical symptoms:
gastralgia, vomiting, dyspepsia, belly aches.
Stomach acu-point of the ear. (see Pg 267)
(see also Many Headed Dryandra)
Physical symptoms: hepatitis, hypochondriac pain, eye diseases.
Liver acu-point on the ear. (see Pg 261)
(see also White Eremophila)

Healing Pathway to the Soul

The Universe gives freely and provides shelter and nourishment for all Life. To go against this dynamic Universal flow is to invite distortion into our own lives. Whenever we stem the tide of giving, our own lives become impoverished, sapped of happiness and sweetness. Focusing on possessions does not give deep or lasting fulfilment and can often be the ruin of a relationship. The spirit of sharing, and finding happiness in seeing the enjoyment of others, leads to a greater sense of the joys of togetherness and oneness.

Meditation Poem

Blue Leschenaultia

I open the door

inviting Life in

to see what I have to offer.

Please let me give more

there is always more coming in

flowing in like an endless stream

and out into the ocean again.

The Sweetness of Appreciation

*Positive Qualities
Key Words:*

tolerance

impartial

kindness

humility

appreciation

*Problem Target
Key Words:*

critical

judgmental

arrogant

superiority

complex

The essence of enjoying people for their uniqueness. To encourage respect and appreciation for people and their intrinsic value. For when intellectual criticism needs to be transformed into acceptance of others, their individual and differing expressions. Allows a sweetness and openness to come into interactions with others rather than judgmental attitudes.

Mind - Common Uses:

Helpful for bridging communication and mutual respect problems in relationships.

For feelings of intellectual superiority.

To deal with the mind that is habituated in dissecting people and their ideas and finding flaws, rather than keeping a positive outlook which discriminates and weighs ideas up without a negative slant.

Also for the mentality which makes hasty judgments of people as fools, or weak minded because these people are not able to "cross swords" as equals with them intellectually.

The healing allows the loving nature of a person to come to the fore and be open to another person's perspectives, conceiving of ideas and way of thinking.

Mind - Floral Acu-pressure

Psychological profile:
Intellectual arrogance.
Forehead acu-point of the ear. (see Pg 253)
Psychological profile: Convinced about the correctness of one's ideas
or knowledge. Feeling correct about one's conceptualization of the
trend things should take or the way things should be.
Lung acu-point of the ear. (see Pg 261)
(use with Yellow Leschenaultia) (see also White Eremophila)

Physical - Floral Acu-pressure

Physical symptoms:
Headache, dizziness, insomnia.
Forehead acu-point of the ear. (see Pg 253)
Physical symptoms: cough, asthma.
Lung acu-point on the ear. (see Pg 261)
(used with Yellow Leschenaultia) (see also White Eremophila)

Healing Pathway to the Soul

Our expanding consciousness can make the mind strong and able to make clear discernments. However when relating to people a basic respect for each Soul and its journey is a solid premise for positive exchanges. Being able to do mental gymnastics is not a sign of expanded consciousness, just as not being intellectually eloquent is not a sign that a person hasn't developed their mind or their spiritual being. Arrogance can lead to spiritual inertia. If we believe we are better than anyone else we live in a self made illusion.

Meditation Poem

Brachycome

Listening to the heart of another

it is easy to understand,

to feel how life has touched them

and left a silken impression

on their being,

intimate and unique.

Positive Qualities
Key Words:

free

release

patience

acceptance

The essence of freeing the mind. To inspire the realization that the journey of Life will bring solutions, one needs patience and acceptance of the "here and now". To relieve the worried mind so it does not miss out on opportunities for Joy in the present.

Problem Target
Key Words:

worry

anxiety

sleeplessness

obsessive

Mind - Common Uses:

For the mind gripped by morbid, anxious or unpleasant thought. Such thoughts can be part of depressed emotional states and mental confusion.
For anxiety that increases in chaotic environments.
For a person whose thought is circular, there is no immediate solution, and yet the mind will not leave it alone. The thought increases because of the energy being put into it and the problem seems to become worse.

The healing releases the mind from the unhealthy focus bringing a sense of relief. There is then restored a natural sense of working things through, or waiting patiently for a new turn of events.

Physical - Common Uses:

Helpful in relieving stress and sleeplessness caused by worry or an over-stimulated thought.
Also tinnitus and impaired hearing. (see over)

Mind - Floral Acu-pressure

Psychological profile:
mental confusion, too much to do. Worried and anxious, chaotic environment.
Kidney acu-point of the ear. (see Pg 260)

Physical - Floral Acu-pressure

Physical symptoms:
tinnitis and impaired hearing.
Kidney acu-point of the ear. (see Pg 260)
(see also Balga, Geraldton Wax, Yellow Leschenaultia)

Healing Pathway to the Soul

One of the illusions of life is that only by doing something can a problem be solved. We are sure we must think or work harder or faster to get relief . Very often a problem is an opportunity to understand something on a deeper level. By absorbing the lessons of a problem and reflecting on what our reactions tell us about ourselves we can make great progress and ensure the same problems/lessons don't continually recur in our lives.

Meditation Poem

Brown Boronia

From the small thought

my mind is transforming

into the Great - the All Possible.

The blades of grass, the stars and I

are all as they should be.

Positive Qualities Key Words:

positivity

optimism

Light

renewal

Problem Target Key Words:

hopelessness

battling

struggle

past pain

Being Surrounded by Light and Love

This essence helps the person to switch on their Light again, that is, to see they must reach out to the beauty around them, and inside of them to feel that it is good to be alive. Whatever the past pain has been, or how ever long a person has been hurting and struggling to go on, positive life experiences wait for them on the horizon. The renewal of hope and optimism, when we are in touch with our inner Light, is always rewarded.

Mind - Common Uses:

For those who feel like giving up on life, giving up the fight for survival because of past painful experiences. The person has often battled on in spite of all the burdens of their memories and now feels that life cannot be worthwhile or fulfilling. The person may be perfectly justified for the way they feel because of the realities of their life. However, the grim attitude of the hopelessness they embrace is a suffering they are adding to their situation.

For a person unable to come to terms with an incident which makes them feel life is not worth living.

The healing rekindles the flame of hope and brings the Light back into the person's life. They are then able to believe and work towards a richly fulfilling Life.

Physical - Common Uses:

To help those with difficult acute or chronic illnesses, i.e. cancer sufferers.

Healing Pathway to the Soul

It is a brave and perhaps naive person who thinks they can understand the meaning behind all the tragedies that befall a person. The Soul has been on a long journey, going through so many transformations on its way home. In reaching out to the Light, to the Love that is embedded in every part of the Universe, the Soul is refreshed and radiates beauty into their Life.

Meditation Poem

Candle of Life

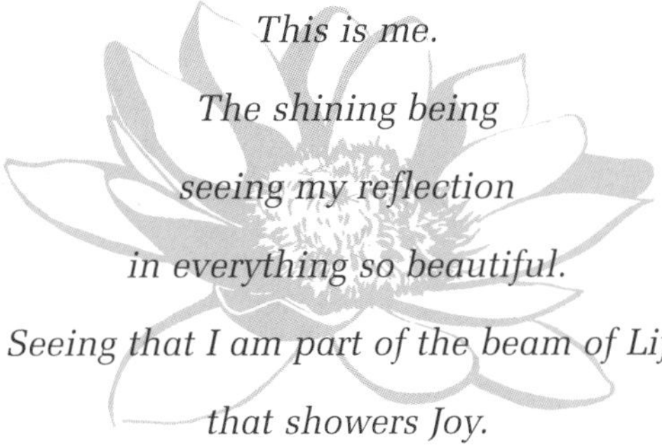

This is me.

The shining being

seeing my reflection

in everything so beautiful.

Seeing that I am part of the beam of Life

that showers Joy.

Positive Qualities Key Words:

Joy

letting go

freeing

geniality

friendly

Problem Target Key Words:

resentment

jealousy

bitterness

envy

blame

Freeing the Past

The essence of enhancing inner renewal and freeing oneself from old baggage that has no part to play in a happy life. For dealing with and healing issues of the past which have left a bitter taste. To re-experience the joy of making the most of possibilities in present and future relationships.

Mind - Common Uses:

For those who are negative and jealous of the happiness of others because their own desires and wishes have been thwarted.
For those who resent other people's happiness because they feel it is unfair that they haven't been that lucky.
For people who have old anger and negativity that has not been resolved. People become cynical and then are unable to attract joy into their lives. Situations from the past may or may not be still affecting their present external reality, but these people can't release their bitterness and so it affects their current relationships with people badly. This can often cause more bitterness and so it goes on, if unhealed.

The healing inspires acceptance in people of their own journey, and love for Life around them, rather than blaming it or others for their predicament.

Physical - Common Uses:

Toxicity, infections. Also used for one of the mind-causes of arthritis and severe rigidity in the body.

Mind - Floral Acu-pressure

Psychological profile:
desire for revenge, hatred.
Uterus acu-point of the ear. (also for men) (see Pg 270)
Psychological profile:
perpetrating sadism, hatred.
Spleen acu-point of the ear. (see Pg 264)
Psychological profile:
Over indulgence, a craving for fulfilment.
Occupit acu-point of the ear. (see Pg 262)

Physical - Floral Acu-pressure

Physical symptoms:
irregular menstruation, leucorrhoea, dysmenorrhoea, impotence,
nocturnal emission.
Uterus acu-point of the ear. (also for men) (see Pg 270)
(see also Macrozamia)
Physical symptoms:
abdominal distension. (use with Pale Sundew)
Spleen acu-point of the ear. (see Pg 264)
(see also Swan River Myrtle)
Physical symptoms: Headache, neurasthenia.
Occupit acu-point of the ear. (see Pg 262)

Healing Pathway to the Soul

One of the signposts of progress on the way to enlightenment is our ability not to get waylaid and caught by belligerence or callousness. If we do not heal ourselves and want to hold on to the pain, and react negatively, we completely lose our way and the whole purpose of our Path. If we do get caught, the quicker we realize how we got into that situation and learn, the easier we will get out and not go into a destructive state of bitterness. We then free ourselves of the past and its effects. This is as equally true in a society as it is in an individual.

Meditation Poem

Cape Bluebell

Oh to feel at ease again,

with the world my friend.

Hard layers are dissolving now,

leaving me

as supple and soft

as a young sapling.

Positive Qualities Key Words:

speaking out

courage

clarity

acknowledgement

Problem Target Key Words:

suppressed

introverted

disregarded

hurt

Speaking Your Truth

This essence encourages the expression of the hurt one feels, so that others may better realize your situation and respond. To lose the fear of communicating pent up gut feelings, and face what is really happening. This allows for the truth to produce clarity, freeing one from both expectation of fairness and the unhealthy situation of being used by others. Helpful for equalizing one sided relationships and bringing reality to obligatory relationships.

Mind - Common Uses:

For those whose opinion is disregarded and as a consequence they suppress their feelings because it seems pointless.
For people who suppress their feelings because they fear rejection if they speak out, however diplomatically and carefully. The person, or people they fear a reaction from, may not even be aware they are taking the person for granted or creating pain.

The healing inspires speaking the truth. This gives others the opportunity to show their true colours, and start being appreciative in a real way, or else pursue their self centred ways, exposed. Either way the hurt person then knows where he or she stands and with the new clarity can take the next steps to resolve the problem.

Physical - Common Uses:

When there is a tight feeling in the belly and stomach, use in oral dose, or apply topically to the area.

Healing Pathway to the Soul

Fear is the bane of the human mind. Although it protects us to some degree from harm (and this is its instinctual purpose), if it is not mastered it dams up the flow of our Life. The subtle fear of being rejected for speaking out about something weakens our inner fire and drive, waylays us in stagnancy. In that stagnant pool problems grow and take up more of our vital force until we bring upon ourselves a crisis. Much healthier is to be vulnerably honest to others and then, from the response you receive, better assess where you stand in your own Life.

Meditation Poem

Cats Paw

From my heart I speak,

the meaning is not hidden.

I say my peace, I give of my mind

Whatever comes my way from this

can only be

the bliss of Truth.

responsible

sharing

caring

maturity

Problem Target Key Words:

irresponsible

selfish

inconsistent

immaturity

Being Part of the Whole

For feeling comfortable with responsibilities. This essence helps settle the person, bringing inner contentment which enhances an enjoyment of the family or group. The person can then fulfil responsibilities and reap the rewards of consistency and shared goals. For issues of responsibility in family and group life where duties and everyday pressures are causing an individual to become distant and avoid their his or her share of the load.

Mind - Common Uses:

For those only focused on their own desires who become uncaring. For a family member who is suddenly feeling trapped by the realities of their life, like in the case of a couple with young children, especially the first child. The person is enjoying being in a family, but would like to have their cake and eat it too. They wish to have the joy and comfort of home life and the freedom of single life. The reality is that you can do that, as long as you keep baking more cakes - you just have to put more effort in to make sure that no one is suffering by your pursuing some private goal. Usually these times of panic are phases of a maturing process and the individual learns to integrate the different aspects of their real needs responsibly into their life.

The healing inspires open heartedness and the shouldering of an individual's part of collective life. The focus becomes re-orientated onto the caring for others.

Healing Pathway to the Soul

Selflessness is a cherished development in our spiritual life. The restless hungry mind gives no peace as it runs after so many desires for itself, one after the other. These desires can seem more inviting when they are out of reach. Once they are gained we want something more, something else. Satisfaction leads to another sense of emptiness. When we stop consciously fuelling our selfish desires, new pathways to happiness open up, and our environment and the people in it reflect Joy.

Meditation Poem

Christmas Tree

We are together

We are part of each other

We move towards the sunrise

hand in hand

My hand will be forever warm

my arms forever open.

The Acceptance of Self

*Positive Qualities
Key Words:*

confidence

Self esteem

learning

acceptance

potential

*Problem Target
Key Words:*

Self recrimination

inferiority complex

The essence to inspire feelings of positivity and self esteem. Being able to learn from mistakes with acceptance and without blame or regret. From inner acceptance - to focus - to success. Helpful for overcoming negative self concepts with ensuing phases of stagnation and depression.

Mind - Common Uses:

For a person who lacks confidence, keeps themselves in an inferior position and doesn't try to improve. They feel they are useless or not good enough and so perpetuate their situation.
For those with an inferiority complex who dump on themselves.
For those lacking confidence.
Very often this essence is used in cases where a person has not been encouraged as a child and doesn't have a good self image. Also in cases where people's experiences in relationships always left them feeling they were not good enough for the other person.

The healing brings a realization of the need to work with one's potentials, to Love and respect oneself, improve oneself and learn from mistakes.

Healing Pathway to the Soul

In the early stages of our development we need to establish who we are and appreciate our own individuality. If we don't establish this then we find there is not enough strength and determination accessible to stride forward on our Path. Feelings of inferiority are an illusion, as all have the perfect expression of the Divine Love deep within.

Meditation Poem

Correa

In the symphony of Life

I sing a note.

It is like no other

and so I give it my all

and hear beautiful music

through all my Life.

Positive Qualities
Key Words:

re-energize

rebuild

vigour

Problem Target
Key Words:

shattered

tired

exhaustion

trauma

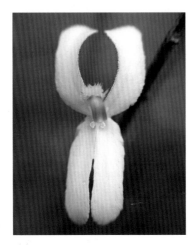

The Restoring

The essence of recovery from trauma. To help rebuild and re-thread the subtle and physical bodies after a shattering experience, mentally and/or physically, thereby energizing them. To integrate such experiences into one's understanding and perspective on Life in a wise way and move forward with renewed vigour.

Mind - Common Uses:

Used in cases where a person has experienced a sudden reversal of fortune. The person has often not made provision for such events, and is therefore not prepared mentally to adapt and deal with the situation. Such people find it hard to rebuild their life and feel hopeless, becoming a victim of circumstance.

The healing will help development of a state of mind that has greater depth and awareness of possibilities. If the person is in a traumatic situation the essence gives the strength to turn life around and rebuild it from the wiser perspective.

Physical - Common Uses:

Used in recovery from trauma.
For mending the etheric body when it experiences shattering.

Mind - Floral Acu-pressure

Psychological profile:
inability to recover emotionally from shock and trauma.
Heart acu-point of the ear. (see Pg 255)
(see also Pink Fountain Triggerplant, Purple Enamel Orchid, Reed Triggerplant.)
Psychological profile: insomnia, dream disturbed sleep, feeling of falling apart, unable to cope.
Shenmen acu-point of the ear. (see Pg 263)

Physical - Floral Acu-pressure

Physical symptoms:
lack of energy after a shock or trauma. After surgery or accidents, or sudden emotional events which are devastating on the physical vitality and cohesion.
Heart acu-point of the ear. (see Pg 255)
(see also Pink Fountain Triggerplant, Purple Enamel Orchid, Reed Triggerplant.)
Physical symptoms:
inflammation, pain.
The Shenmen acu-point of the ear. (see Pg 263)
(can be used with Pink Fairy Orchid, Hybrid Pink Fairy Orchid, Reed Triggerplant, Pink Fountain Triggerplant, Violet Butterfly) (see also Purple Flag Flower and Yellow Flag Flower)

Healing Pathway to the Soul

Optimism is a great benefit to our Life. Awareness of the possibilities of the ups and downs that can occur gives us the advantage of readiness to respond when fortunes change and the changes then don't have the effect of hampering our forward movement. Optimism without awareness and a higher perspective can mean a foolhardy approach that is vulnerable to upsets. We then feel depleted. Far better to keep our enthusiasm and zest for Life while taking into account the many experiences Life can manifest.

Meditation Poem

Cowkicks

My inner light guides me

through the pathway of my Life

Whole and at one

I raise my eyes to see all

and understand where and how

to place each foot forward.

Positive Qualities Key Words:

humility

confidence

Self assured

inner satisfaction

Problem Target Key Words:

demanding

selfish

attention seeking

competitive

The Acceptance of All as Equals

To discover the truth that all are equal. This essence helps resolve problems of over-competitiveness and brings a person into a space to freely interact with others as an equal. The Self then comes from a deeper aspect where it can feel joy for another's successes without feeling inferior or unattended. For issues of craving recognition and acceptance from others.

Mind - Common Uses:

For those who tend to demand attention, respect and recognition. For a person who is craving acknowledgement and becomes negative when people don't respond on cue. Such people need to be constantly told what a good job they have done, or how good they are. Mixed in with this are flashes of superiority complex, over estimation of self-importance and a dismissing of people as underlings. Phases of all these traits are common in childhood, especially where parents have tended to placate the child and not deal with the negative behaviour. The demands then continue to rise to new levels.

The healing brings a quieting of the mind, which can feel Self assurance and inner contentment.

Mind - Floral Acu-pressure

Psychological profile:
superiority complex, dictatorial.
Heart acu-point of the ear. (see Pg 255)

Psychological profile:
mind drawn too quickly onto anything in their surroundings, too externally concentrated, overly alert.
Eye acu-point of the ear. (see Pg 253)

Physical - Floral Acu-pressure

Physical symptoms:
Hysteria, palpitation, arrhythmia.
Heart acu-point of the ear. (see Pg 255)
(see also Ursinia)

Physical symptoms:
Eye diseases eye strain, problems focussing.
Eye acu-point of the ear. (see Pg 253)

Healing Pathway to the Soul

The Light of consciousness is the essence within every being. We need to recognize the Light within ourselves, and it does not matter if this Light is recognized by others. It is, and always will be. Similarly those other persons can be seen with their inner Light shining. There is no scope for feeling inferior or superior. Such thoughts are an illusion of the mind trapped in a state of smallness.

Meditation Poem

Cowslip Orchid

I salute you - every living being

every rock and star.

Thank you for being part of this

world I enjoy.

The Freedom of Letting Go

To be open to the many streams of happiness and fulfilment, to be enriched by being flexible. The essence of letting go and allowing Life to flow. Helpful in times of change, grief and reconciliation, to allow the old day to go and the new day to be embraced with flexibility.

Positive Qualities
Key Words:

flexibility

open

co-operative

letting go

Problem Target
Key Words:

rigidity

suppressive

serious

uptight

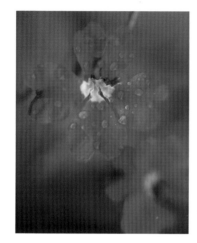

Mind - Common Uses:

For problems of general stress, inflexibility, not being able to adapt to new situations, stress and tension through wanting things a certain way and no other.
For parting trauma such as grief, separation, divorce.
For those who are unco-operative unless things are done their way.
For issues of holding on and rigidity of mind and body. For releasing the need that Life and people should conform to only one perspective for you to be satisfied, comfortable or happy.

The healing inspires the letting go of concepts that restrict the mind bringing a new quality of flexibility. Accepting and working with new attitudes becomes increasingly easier. There are then new possibilities for being deeply fulfilled and enjoying relationships with others.

Physical - Common Uses:

Hard, tight muscles, cramps and spasms used directly on area. Used direct to back of neck and shoulders to relieve headaches caused by tension in these areas. Applied to lower abdomen to relieve constipation, oral doses for chronic problem. Is part of the formula for flower essence Pain Cream.

Physical - Floral Acu-pressure

Physical symptoms:
spasm, cramping and painful areas on the muscles adjacent to spine, neck and joints.
Spinal, Neck and Joints acu-points on the ear.
(see Pgs 256-259, 265-266)
(see also Purple Flag Flower, Leafless Orchid, Menzies Banksia and Macrozamia, Ursinia.)

Healing Pathway to the Soul

When we hold on to rigid concepts of what we think is going to be right or what will make us happy we hamper our own evolution and with it the happiness of others. With an open mind we can look at many options and even try out new avenues of joy. When we explore our Life openly we learn what true depth of happiness is. Also we develop the wisdom and understanding to manifest it in our world.

Meditation Poem

DAMPIERA

When the bindings of my own mind

trapped the flow of joy

You opened me up

to the freedom of seeing

the potential of happiness

in every opportunity.

Positive Qualities
Key Words:

detachment

peace

positivity

release

rebuild trust

Problem Target
Key Words:

blaming

resentment

revenge

wronged

suspicious

The Inner Resolution

The essence to invoke Life affirming positivity, to release thoughts about being wronged in the past. To find detachment and be at peace within oneself and not be reacting from vengeful emotions. To find release in the realization that one has a choice in how to respond to events, and that to harbour blame hardens the heart. To find mellowness of being and take responsibility for a better tomorrow.

Mind - Common Uses:

For those who can't get rid of the "chip on their shoulder", and hold on to feelings of revenge against those who have wronged them.
For those who cannot have trust in new relationships because of their experiences in the past.
For those who believe there is satisfaction in revenge.
The vengeful, jilted lover.
For people who have taken vengeful actions against a person they love and now are sickened by it. They now regret they have hurt someone they cared for and feel that Life has set them up to have pain.
For those who blame Life and other people for their misfortunes. This leads to cutting off from sensitivity and openness.

The healing brings a realization that we are responsible for our actions and reactions to Life. That there is a benevolent basis to Life with which we must work to achieve happiness, healing ourselves of past pains. We can then walk away from the thoughts of being wronged and/or the people who have wronged us and start living positively, with an open heart, for today.

Healing Pathway to the Soul

A seeming paradox is the idea that we can be detached and yet at the same time be vulnerable. Detached in the positive sense means to let go of anything harmful or unnecessary, and to be vulnerable in the positive sense is to be open to Love. When painful events happen both these qualities of detachment and vulnerability ensure that we can make it through to the other side healed and intact, with our loving nature stronger and even more vibrant. Hardening, or becoming bitter and resentful keeps the pain with us constantly. Far better to feed the positive qualities and move on.

Meditation Poem

Donkey Orchid

What has happened

is behind me.

Forward go my thoughts

to days of Joy

and nights of Peace

with blissful dreams.

ositive Qualities
Key Words:

gracious

giving

loving

Problem Target
Key Words:

demanding

self-centred

resentful

tantrums

The Grateful Heart

For the building of a gracious, loving nature. This essence stimulates love and focus out towards others. One becomes happy by giving, balancing a perspective that has led to introversion, being demanding, and over concentrated on oneself and what one has, or has not got.

Mind - Common Uses:

For those who use the emotions to manipulate situations and people so their wants can be satisfied.

For problems of greed, thirst for acquisition.

For people who become brooding, revengeful and manipulative to create a pressure to get what they want. They want Life to run around them, and react badly when friends and family get sick of their ways and let them know it.

For demanding children who create tantrums to wear down their parents, and have their wants met.

For people who feel they can only get love by applying pressure and manipulating people.

The healing stimulates the love aspect and consequently decentralizes focus on oneself. When the realization occurs that it is the selfish, desireful state of mind and being that is creating the unhappy reality, the person changes his or her ways.

95

Mind - Floral Acu-pressure

Psychological profile:
jealousy, feeling you should have what your peers have, and resentful
when you haven't.
Tongue acu-point of the ear. (see Pg 269)

Healing Pathway to the Soul

Once people believed that the Sun circled around the Earth. It was a
natural perspective to take, due to the limited expansion of
consciousness back in the times of Galileo, who, through a humble
outward reaching mind, saw that the Earth was the one who circled
the Sun. We too can live in an illusory perspective that Life revolves
around us and our needs, or that it should. The real serenity lies in
gratefully knowing that the whole Universe is flowing within and
without us, giving to all, as does our spiritual Self.

Meditation Poem

Fringed Lily Twiner

So many gifts

have been given

to my heart.

Morning Sun

a kind eye

and the smiles of friends.

Positive Qualities Key Words:

benevolence

good intentions

conscience

straight forward

Problem Target Key Words:

interfering

nosey

gossiping

deceptive

control

Choosing Benevolence

For the mind to embrace benevolence and good intentions. This essence frees the conscience which then naturally brings the mind back to balanced, healthy pursuits. For those who find themselves caught in unhealthy curiosity about the affairs of others, who feel powerful with personal information and can't resist using it for their own ends.

Mind - Common Uses:

For those focused on petty things about others and cause damage by loose talk. They like the control they have when privy to personal information. This makes such people very unpopular and causes complicated emotional situations. In extreme cases they are very smug and feel superior because they can be the cause of such havoc through having such control over people's lives. Often these people come for healing because of rejection or hatred from others, be it in the school yard or the boardroom.

For those who enjoy controlling others, manipulating behind the scenes.

The healing brings a realization that control of other people is unhealthy and distasteful. A feeling then predominates that these types of pursuits are totally wrong and they bring their conscience into play, and pay attention to the more beautiful, straight forward and honest approach to relationships.

Healing Pathway to the Soul

As we all are within the mind of the Creator, there is nothing we can do that is not witnessed. However smart a person may think they are, they will painfully find out about their illusion as the rest of Life responds naturally and inexorably to their deeds.

Meditation Poem

Fringed Mantis Orchid

I see where I have gone wrong.

The mind should always be

an instrument bringing honesty.

This I can do now

that I realize

my mistake.

ositive Qualities
Key Words:

unifying

truthful

honesty

integrity

expression

Problem Target
Key Words:

two-faced

hypocrisy

hidden negativity

smug

The Unity of Thought, Word and Deed

For the Self to be unified in all expressions. The essence to find the freedom of showing one's true thoughts and intentions. To be able to think, say, and be as one whole person without hiding any underlying negativity and thereby falling into hypocrisy.

Mind - Common Uses:

Used for character traits of two faced behaviour, where such people harbour negativity but show nothing of this towards those they dislike. Being able to trick people in this way leads to added attitudes of thinking other people are stupid. If exposed such people become more negative.

For those who feel amused by the misfortunes of others while pretending to be sympathetic. They feel contemptuous towards those they see as fools.

The healing enables them to let go of their negative thought patterns and see it as only fair that other people confront them and expect more honesty and integrity. They then can be straightforward in their dealings with people.

Healing Pathway to the Soul

The unifying of thought, word and deed is a major development in a spiritual aspirant. Until such time as this unity occurs the duality or triality of each of these aspects creates disharmony and often pain and suffering for ourselves and others. When we are honest in our inward and outward expression, we allow maximum potential for transformation, because, as Life responds to us, we can consciously see what is wrong or unfair in our attitudes, and then change. Those who think one thing, say another and do yet another, are a long way from enjoying Life. Facing up to the consequences of our thoughts frees us to new and better thought, and a new and better reality.

Meditation Poem

Fuchsia Grevillea

As I think so I become.
To fill the mind with loving thoughts
brings loving words
brings loving deeds
in such a world I want to live.

comfortable

at ease

accepting

contemplate

**Problem Target
Key Words:**

fearful

claustrophobia

trapped

irrational

panic

Freedom from Claustrophobia

To be free to be comfortable and at peace, even when restricted. The essence for claustrophobia, both physical and emotional. To enable a person not to feel panic in a confined space or when feeling under threat. To allow the rush of energy and fear to be earthed so rational thought can prevail.

Mind - Common Uses:

Used in cases where a person is suffering from claustrophobia. Fear of being enclosed. Inability to go on aircraft, in tunnels, small rooms etc. For fear of being trapped in a smothering relationship.
For a fearfulness and anxiety that life is closing in and there are no solutions.

The healing frees the mind from the irrational adrenaline response and the mind can then think clearly and calmly.

Physical - Common Uses:

Sweating and hypertension caused by fear of being trapped.

Healing Pathway to the Soul

We are always free, it is only our perception of a situation that makes us feel a prisoner. Nothing can imprison our Soul.

Meditation Poem

Fuchsia Gum

I am free to go anywhere at will.

Like a breeze

or a sunbeam.

My mind takes me

to the beautiful places

whenever I like.

Positive Qualities Key Words:

inner strength

independent

self assured

Problem Target Key Words:

influenced

pressured

dominated

obligatory

The Sanctity of the Self

The essence of inner strength and being what you know is true to yourself. To feel the beauty of being strong against the wind of adverse opinion and pressure. To strengthen oneself so as not to be pressured against one's will, or be routinely influenced by the desires of others who focus on you.

Mind - Common Uses:

Helpful for dominant/submissive relationships.
For adolescents succumbing to peer group pressure.
For people who are going against what they suspect or know inside to be fair or true.
To help people learn to stand their ground and not compromise themselves under coercion.
To free a person who is bowing to another's will.

The healing enhances, and brings up, the inner strength and assuredness, and one can feel content that they are being their own person.

Physical - Common Uses:

Used in cases where the immune system is weakened by sickness or drugs.

Mind - Floral Acu-pressure

Psychological profile:
over accommodating other's opinions or ideas, listening too much to others.
Internal Ear acu-point of the ear. (see Pg 255)
Psychological profile:
Feeling useless, helpless, unable to achieve.
Brain stem acu-point of the ear. (see Pg 250)

Physical - Floral Acu-pressure

Physical symptoms:
tinnitis, impaired hearing. (see also Yellow Leschenaultia)
Internal Ear acu-point of the ear. (see Pg 255)
Physical symptoms: Headache, vertigo.
Brain stem acu-point of the ear. (see Pg 250)

Healing Pathway to the Soul

We learn as we live, so many things. Often we learn a particular truth and then a test may come as to whether we will now live by that truth. If there is a person in our life who doesn't want us to walk that path they will put pressure on us verbally or non verbally by moods and actions. With inner strength such pressure has no effect, except to make clear to us what our journey should be and where the other person is coming from.

Meditation Poem

Geraldton Wax

Within me

the deep rosy glow of my being

speaks to me of my unassailable Soul.

I walk my Life

lighting my way as I go.

regeneration

optimism

inspiration

joyous

Problem Target Key Words:

sadness

abused

heaviness

hopelessness

The Spirit of Regeneration

To find the powers of regeneration and metamorphosis within. The essence to care for and heal oneself so one can bounce back after personal trauma and unload the feelings of heaviness. When this is achieved the renewed inspiration for Life and zest for living carries one through to positive experiences and gives scope for great fulfilment.

Mind - Common Uses:

For people who feel weighed down by the murky areas of their Life and have lost the ability to feel good about living. The such persons have often been of a very giving nature, been highly traumatized, hurt and battered by life, been taken for granted and abused, which leads to them wanting to withdraw from people. Life becomes too hard so they don't want to interact with it any more. In extreme cases there is often a subconscious desire to no longer be on this earth.

The healing brings a person back in touch with the goodness of Life and the positive aspects which can be so joyous and fulfilling, regenerating hope and idealism.

Physical - Common Uses:

Used topically over internal areas of the body affected by degeneration, e.g. cancer.

Mind - Floral Acu-pressure

Psychological profile:
indiscriminate giving, leaving oneself open to being exploited.
Tongue acu-point of the ear. (see Pg 269)

Healing Pathway to the Soul

To keep in touch with the source of regeneration, Light and Love, is to be continually renewed. If we focus our minds on our suffering, this perspective will take us out of touch with the very instrument of healing that we need. Whatever has happened to us in our past can be healed, and we don't have to carry that darkness with us on the rest of our journey. After a dark experience we must care for ourselves, heal ourselves, regain our vigour and move on towards the sunrise of the rest of our Life.

Meditation Poem

Giving Hands

My sinking heart

has now risen.

Sunning itself in the day

and resting peacefully at night.

I feel so young,

a tender bud uncurling.

The Strength of the Patient Heroine

Positive Qualities Key Words:

mature

nurturing

patient

supportive

unconditional Love

Problem Target Key Words:

overbearing

hard

judgmental

severe

manipulative

emotional

clinging

dependent

For the maturing of the female principle or woman within. For both men and women a metamorphosis to inner strength, nurturing sensitivity, patience and loving wisdom that is not emotionally dependent. Helpful in releasing the feminine aspect into society.

Mind - Common Uses:

For people who are either unable to bring out their nurturing, compassionate or patient side (underactive unbalanced feminine aspect) or who tend to resort only to their emotions to deal with relationships (overactive unbalanced feminine aspect).
Also for issues of mothering, such as using guilt to maintain control, not allowing independence for those in one's care, or the other extreme of not being able to enjoy caring for and nurturing someone who is vulnerable, and in need of help.
First time mothers can be caught in such dilemmas and during pregnancy or early days of motherhood feel totally alien to the new role before them.

The healing, for men and women, is the maturing of the feminine aspect of strength which is necessary for a balanced attitude to oneself, to others, and to relationships. This creates a strength which is nurturing, caring, and yet helping to bring out strength in the other person.

Physical - Common Uses:

Used in cases of menstrual abnormalities and female hormone imbalances.

Mind - Floral Acu-pressure

Psychological Profile:
Strong desire to have physical sexual experiences with another's body, overconfident, "stud" or "Macho" mentality that thinks "I'm good at this".
Testes / Ovaries acu-point of the ear. (see Pg 268)
The healing opens the heart to feelings and sex becomes a two way experience for both to enjoy.

Physical - Floral Acu-pressure

Physical symptoms:
Epididymitis, irregular menstruation.
Testes / Ovaries acu-point of the ear. (see Pg 268)

Healing Pathway to the Soul

The instant response to shelter and protect that which is not yet strong, brings out the Universal Mother within us. In this way we reflect the gentle principle which has sheltered us along our way and pays respect to the Life force which nurtures everything in Creation. We then show the qualities of patience and understanding which greatly comfort fellow travellers.

Meditation Poem

Goddess Grasstree

I am a rock that faces the storm

the warmth that gives Life the hand that guides

the words that relieve.

I have the strength to endure

yet the softness to love without end.

open

sociable

confident

expressive

detached

**Problem Target
Key Words:**

withdrawing

aversion

shy

wary

cut off

The Coming Out

The essence of opening up and opening out. Feeling the dignity of coming forward to take your place in Life, regardless of being vulnerable to exposure. To be at ease with yourself while being with other people and not fear being open. Confidence for those who feel more comfortable withdrawing from people than dealing with problems or criticism. Enables one to detach from the tangled situations and judgmental attitudes of others and instead feel free to join in social situations.

Mind - Common Uses:

For those who fear being exposed and are therefore wary of being open and vulnerable to others.

For those who hang back, tired of the turbulence of interactions with people and all the trouble that can be. Often they are not conscious that this is why they are a "background" person, but they usually feel the lack of confidence. They have perhaps been open and relaxed previously and this very characteristic has been used to their detriment by others. Now they feel the best solution is to shut people out. This keeps other people out of their affairs. If they are vulnerable or in a mess no one will know and be able to hurt them.

For children who don't speak much, or at all, whom others may label as shy, who can be withdrawing from what they see as disturbing and confusing aspects of adults' lives which they are part of.

For those who seem shy, but are really very wary of other people and of what can happen when allowing someone into their world.

For a person who feels unnecessarily modest, feeling shame about the naturalness of their body.

The healing brings a feeling of ease and openness in being part of other people's lives, with a healthy sense of detachment and perspective on any difficulties that may arise. There comes with this a confidence in being able to handle such events without any fear of the personal exposure that this situation may bring.

Mind - Floral Acu-pressure

Psychological profile:
Pretending to cope but masking the reality of one's inability to handle life internally and/or externally.
Urinary Bladder acu-point of the ear. (see Pg 269

Physical - Floral Acu-pressure

Physical symptoms: enuresis, retention of urine.
(use with Hairy Yellow Pea)
Urinary Bladder acu-point of the ear. (see Pg 269
(see also Hairy Yellow Pea)

Healing Pathway to the Soul

Life in society is a picnic to which all need to bring their "goodies" - their special and unique contributions to the collective flow. If some cannot contribute something to the feast because of past unpleasant experiences of exposure, then the whole society misses out on their talents.

Meditation Poem

Golden Glory Grevillea

Taking a step out from the shadows,

face uplifted.

I can breathe the scented air

feel the warmth of Life on my naked being

free of shame o fear and know that all is well.

The world waits for me to begin.

broadening

carefree

expansive

adaptable

**Problem Target
Key Words:**

perfectionism

worry

petty

small perspective

Expanding Horizons

The essence to take the mind beyond small peripheral issues. To re-ignite carefree feelings, to heal all aspects of anxiety linked to perfectionism. Helpful for those who worry about details, allowing the mind to become bright and inquisitive, positive in outlook, and adaptable to changing needs.

Mind - Common Uses:

For people who are continually caught in over-attention to small matters and small details in big matters. The perspective they have increases a negative and hopeless state where problems can never be solved because there is always another detail to consider.
For those caught in small details which can create low energy states, depressed states, anxious states and totally frustrated states of mind.
For those who feel overconfident in their ability to assess because of their attention to detail, but really are at a disadvantage because of their myopic perspective.

The healing allows the mind to free itself from the small, tight framework. When the person is freed from the small perspective, problems can often dissolve because it was the unnecessary focus that was making the problem in the first place.

Physical - Common Uses:

For those needing to accept their present imperfect state of health and well being, while convalescing from illness or trauma Golden Waitsia can be applied to the soles of the feet every few hours.
(no pressure needed to application, simply wipe essence over entire sole of foot)

Healing Pathway to the Soul

Giving care to the big and small aspects of Life creates a balance, but giving priority to the small aspects brings stagnancy and a feeling of treading water. The spiritual perspective gives all care to the small details but only in the greater scheme of things. The focus is on the deeper underlying flow of issues not the ever-changing shapes of the waves on the surface.

Meditation Poem

Golden Waitsia

The greatness of the Universe

the fullness of existence

can only be fathomed

by my mind

expanding freely

to be embraced by Peace.

Moving Forward

Positive Qualities
Key Words:

breakthrough

change

progress

focus

vigour

Problem Target
Key Words:

indolent

stagnation

resentment

defeated

The essence of making progress, of focusing ahead and using vigour to accomplish a breakthrough. To enhance forward movement through a problem, or phase of stagnation, without sudden leaps back to square one. To be free of frustration, to help fight listlessness and the repetition of mistakes. Helpful in maintaining disciplines and healthy habits for body, mind and spirit.

Mind - Common Uses:

For people who cannot successfully complete a change they need to make. They seem to do well but can make surprising reversals and be back where they were in the beginning. This is due to the fact that a strong part of their mind can't be bothered changing, resents having to change, and would prefer to stay the same, if only there were not consequences that were unpleasant. Often the natural consequences are the natural reactions from others, which can make these people negative and defensive towards those around them. This projecting blame onto others can then create within self righteous attitudes and give them a reason to stay stubbornly the way they are.
For those with an indolent attitude.
For those who are battling addictions or addictive patterns of behaviour and are frustrated that they always end up where they started.

The healing helps to strengthen the mind to deal with itself, the attitudes producing frustrating cycles of defeat and to correct the focus onto mastering the inner enemy of one's happiness and putting vigour into endeavours.

Used as a complementary essence with the Blue China Orchid to enhance breaking free of old habits.

113

Mind - Floral Acu-pressure

Used to complement Blue China Orchid work with breaking addictions and unhealthy or unhelpful patterns of living.
The Shenmen acu-point of the ear. (see Pg 263)

Healing Pathway to the Soul

The eternal transformation and growth of everything in creation is the very dynamism of Life. No one can afford to lag behind, caught in a false sense of the security of what has been before. Only expansion into greater levels of awareness and challenging our Self to progress brings the inner serenity and Joy.

Meditation Poem

Green Rose

Within me certainty is awakening

my conviction comes from within.

I will cast aside my old rags

cut myself loose from the chains

and make the future my own.

Positive Qualities Key Words:

decision

patience

direction

wisdom

calm

Problem Target Key Words:

anxious

scattered

overwhelmed

inexperienced

Waiting for the Wave

The art of timing and decision making. The essence of patience in finding direction in Life which leads to peaceful settling of the mind. This patience allows time for the consolidation of experiences so one can make decisions with greater wisdom and determination, and not be influenced into erratic action driven by one's own anxiety.

Mind - Common Uses:

For the person anxiously facing choices they are not ready to make. For those who are trying to keep many activities going because they are unsure of which ones to focus on.

For people anxious about the choices in front of them. There are times when a they have to make a decision or choices about their life but are not in the position to do so wisely. It can be that they are young, inexperienced, amidst other crises, or unable to see the wood for the trees. With the enhancement of patience and a stilled mind, the person can make interim decisions, waiting for the right time, to read the flow of Life correctly and make their move.

Helpful to enhance the intuitive understanding of one's Life direction.

The healing enables the mind to settle and be patient until enough understanding is developed to make wise choices.

Mind - Floral Acu-pressure

Psychological profile:
believing one cannot achieve, feelings of being in a mess or devastated.
Cannot see how things will work out.
The Urinary Bladder acu-point of the ear. (see Pg 269)

Physical - Floral Acu-pressure

Physical symptoms:
enuresis, retention of urine.
The Urinary Bladder acu-point of the ear. (see Pg 269)
(used with Golden Glory Grevillea) (see also Golden Glory Grevillea)

Healing Pathway to the Soul

We can spend our whole life waiting to be ready. It is the small steps
we take while assessing Life from the deepest perspective that help us
to be fully part of Life and also to be learning at the same time. Then
when the more poignant moments of opportunity come, we recognise
them and make the most of them.

Meditation Poem

Hairy Yellow Pea

A calm encircles me.

I feel an inner assurance

all will be well

all is to be

revealed in the

blossoming of my Self.

The Freedom of Independence

Positive Qualities
Key Words:

Self assured

independent

determination

capable

Problem Target
Key Words:

trepidation

insecure

under-confidence

emotionally
dependent

The spirit of self assurance, the realisation of self reliance and determination. To inspire standing on one's own feet, to be able to believe in and achieve with one's own strength. To believe in one's own ability to attract into the Self that which one needs. Helpful for trepidation about striking out on a new path less travelled by others, being able to let go of the need for a backup person or simply fear of doing things alone.

Mind - Common Uses:

For people who find it too challenging to do things by themselves. They feel more comfortable when someone else is with them.
For those who in one area of their life do not feel confident enough to follow a new path which the majority of people around them do not tread..
For people who do not have confidence in their ability to attract a partner into their life and so do not project themselves in a way that anyone can notice them.
Also for those who are not confident that they can attract a partner simply by being themselves, and instead project bravado and try to use an over assertive or dominating approach.

The healing enables an appreciation of the Self, its power to withstand the thorns on the road, and to accept the inner beauty of individuality. The belief in the Self and its potential, opens up opportunities for experiencing greater happiness.

Mind - Floral Acu-pressure

Psychological profile:
looking for support from others, failing in one's own endeavours
because there is no support from others. Feeling let down.
Small Intestine acu-point of the ear. (see Pg 264)

Physical - Floral Acu-pressure

Physical symptoms:
dyspepsia, palpitation
Small Intestine acu-point of the ear. (see Pg 264)
(see also Yellow Flag Flower)

Healing Pathway to the Soul

No one in this Universe is ever alone. Eternally with, and integral to
us, is the Consciousness of the Great. Although insignificant if we try
to make our little "i" seem vast and important, when we flow as part
of the Universal "I" there is nothing we can be afraid of. The
individual Soul on its journey is continually attracting Life to itself.
The beauty of its individuality as part of the Universal Soul ensures its
success.

Meditation Poem

Happy Wanderer

As I walk

I hear the encouragement

of a voice within saying

My love for you,

beautiful one,

is always there.

The Mind at Rest

Positive Qualities
Key Words:

relaxation

release

rest

peace

Problem Target
Key Words:

frenetic

hyper

over-active

scattered energy

stress

The essence of relaxation and release. Earthing excessive scattered energy and re-establishing a natural and healthy flow which feeds the needs of activity, without over stimulating the mind. With this inner mental and physical peace one feels back in control of one's Life and can have balanced states of rest and activity.

Mind - Common Uses:

Used in cases of the frenetic, active person. The hyperactive child. For people who have been in fearful or over-stimulated states for a long period of time and now they can't relax their body or mind when they need to.

When the etheric body is too highly strung you find people who are naturally tense and affected by the little inconsequential happenings in their life. This over-stimulates their nervous system and they find it hard to relax. They can often see no cause as to why they are unable to switch off.

This essence relaxes the etheric body and thereby relaxes unbalanced nerve activity.

Physical - Common Uses:

For those who can't sleep or relax due to frenetic (red) energy unbalancing them. Six drops of the essence in a half glass of water, a couple of drops on the back of the head hourly from 4pm to bedtime to enhance sleep.

Healing Pathway to the Soul

We can sometimes forget the reality that our mind directly and indirectly is the master of our body, the master of our brain. We also can forget that the Soul is the master of our mind. When the parallelism between body and mind waves lose their synchronicity we feel the havoc on every level. It is at these times that we can appreciate the need to be more in touch with the deepest part of our being which creates harmony between our body, mind and Spirit.

Meditation Poem

Hops Bush

Still is my mind

lying in the lap

of my serene Soul.

The waves of bliss

cool and refresh me.

**Positive Qualities
Key Words:**

inner strength

discriminating

resilient

stability

**Problem Target
Key Words:**

oversensitive

influenced

reactionary

emotional

The Glow of the Inner Being

The essence of knowing who you are, the sanctity of your inner being, the strength to maintain your inner peace no matter where you are, or what circumstances may be there to influence your judgement about your Self. This essence is as a filter and inner strengthener, so that a person is not going up and down with the praise or condemnation of others. For those who feel keenly the feelings of others. Also for those psychically sensitive, it helps to relieve the burden of that sensitivity by engendering a contentment generated by their own centre.

Mind - Common Uses:

Used for cases of stress resulting from interactions with people.
For those who wish they could maintain their inner peace and not go up and down with other people's emotions. Often there can be anger, tears or frustration at the continual stress of the emotional see-saw.
For those who are oversensitive and tend to react out of proportion to others words and deeds.
For premenstrual syndrome and sensitivity of feeling in pregnancy, creating a rosy glow of inner tranquillity.
Also for those wishing to overcome nervousness when speaking in public or expressing their views to others.
Also used with Macrozamia essence for the emotional fluctuations of adolescence and menopause.

Physical - Common Uses:

For cases of lowered immunity, high allergy responses, skin problems and hypertension. A general stress essence.

Mind - Floral Acu-pressure

Psychological profile:
feelings of falling apart, unable to cope.
The Shenmen acu-point of the ear. (see Pg 263)

Psychological profile:
feeling of wanting to be left alone, oversensitive towards others,
overreacting to people, unable to maintain perspective.
Duodenum acu-point of the ear. (see Pg 252)

Physical - Floral Acu-pressure

Physical symptoms:
insomnia, dream disturbed sleep, inflammation, pain.
The Shenmen acu-point of the ear. (see Pg 263)
Can be used with Pink Fairy Orchid, Pink Fountain Triggerplant,
Cowkicks, Reed Triggerplant, Violet Butterfly   (see also Purple Flag
Flower and Yellow Flag Flower)

Physical symptoms:
Duodenal ulcer, pylorospasm
Duodenum acu-point of the ear. (see Pg 252)
(see also Red Leschenaultia)

Healing Pathway to the Soul

There is a fine line between being sensitive and in touch with Life and not having a strong internal guidance to steer our course. If sensitivity means we don't know who we are, and we go with whatever strong emotions are around us, we can lose our way. When the Self is radiating from the centre of our being we can remain sensitive to all Life around us, to people and their feelings and needs, but can choose with wisdom our responses.

Meditation Poem

Hybrid Pink Fairy Orchid

All around is swirling Life

a thousand faces

and out stretched beckoning hands.

Yet the silent centre

remains tranquil

drawing Love from its depths.

Fearless Contemplation

**Positive Qualities
Key Words:**

fearless

Joy

bright

exuberant

fun

realization

**Problem Target
Key Words:**

downcast

hurt

avoiding

fear

suppressed memory

The essence of valour to overcome painful memories hiding in the subconscious. The essence of Joy and courage to face and deal with past shadows and pain. To inspire the knowledge that there is no hidden pain that can't be dealt with, it is never as bad as you fear, it will not overwhelm you, you are stronger than it.

Mind - Common Uses:

For people who are living without being able to feel Joy, there is hidden pain, like a dark cloud, casting a shadow over them. Some past experience, which they consciously remember or which lies in their subconscious, has not been healed.
To help people get through the healing of painful memories.
For suppressed memory.
For those who avoid dealing with current situations, the suppressed cause being painful memories.
Helpful also in psychotherapy, rebirthing and past life therapy to uncover forgotten or hidden experiences affecting the present state of being.

Healing Pathway to the Soul

The subconscious pain of past experiences can cast a shadow over our lives. Joy is then always tinged with sadness, or even not able to be felt at all. It is in the hidden recesses of our own mind, where thoughts and all the atmospheres, emotions and triggers to other scenes from our past are held. We must take up the task to heal ourselves. The dragon we are facing is really just ourselves, our unconscious fears. When we finally face the dragon we see that it was not so fearsome, and healing ourselves we can enjoy and appreciate our Life.

Meditation Poem

Illyarrie

Pain is a prickle bush

that catches on my mind.

I release each thorn

it is not part of me.

I go on my way.

Positive Qualities
Key Words:

centering

energizing

balance

sustain

wholeness

Problem Target
Key Words:

depleted

tired

worn out

drained

overwhelmed

Control from the Centre

The essence of centralizing energy and focus, to ensure the maintenance of wholeness. Stimulating the inner core of one's being to take control of Life situations. It helps one to withdraw from peripheral concerns and focus on what is of primary importance. The effect is to deepen understanding of what caring for and helping a person can really mean, to know also when to stand back for that person's deeper welfare. Helpful for feelings of depletion in those whose work or life is in the service of others.

Mind - Common Uses:

For people who tend to "give themselves away", and find they are exhausted in every way, and have to get away from people to allow recuperation, and this is not always possible. Very often these are care-givers in "people" jobs such as therapists, nurses, teachers, parents, group organizers. The unbalanced response comes from a lack of proper and considered perspective, although coming from a benevolent desire to be of help.

For benevolent people suffering from "burn out".

For those who fail to deal with the primary causes of their problems.

For those (sometimes termed "do-gooders") who help others but more in a peripheral way and not really in a way that is deep or meaningful. This means they have to keep giving away their time and energy which could have been utilized, for the other person, much more wisely.

The healing brings a person to their centre from where they ascertain deeply the needs of individuals and individual situations. Any efforts are then not wasted and the frugality keeps energy at a constant.

126

Physical - Common Uses:

For people who have a tendency to sacrifice their energy for, or with other people, past the point of healthy balance.

For people recuperating from illness who are drained by visitors because they are trying to give out to them instead of remaining in a quiet self regenerating mode.

Mind - Floral Acu-pressure

Psychological profile:
people who gives out as much as they can in every situation, whether that amount is needed or not.
Baihui acu-point on the head. (see Pg 272)
Psychological profile:
lack of verbal control, saying things at inopportune moments, nervous eating habits, like picking at food.
Mouth acu-point on the ear. (see Pg 262)

Physical - Floral Acu-pressure

Physical symptoms:
feeling drained and tired after interactions with people.
Baihui acu-point on the head. (see Pg 272)
Physical symptoms:
facial paralysis, ulceration of the mouth.
Mouth acu-point on the ear. (see Pg 262)
(see also Pale Sundew)
Physical symptoms:
painful areas on the muscles adjacent to spine, neck and joints.
Spinal, Neck and Joints acu-points on the ear.
(see Pgs 256-259, 265-266)
(see also Dampiera, Purple Flag Flower, Menzies Banksia and Macrozamia, Ursinia.)

Healing Pathway to the Soul

There are many ways in which we can help ourselves and others. What may superficially at first seem like a need can really mask other problems. We need to take an overview into account to be really of productive help. Taking the higher and more all encompassing perspective, and coming from a calm centre, we can assess the primary needs and give exactly that which is required for the real need.

Meditation Poem

Leafless Orchid

My awareness is always there.

Sometimes silent,

sometimes tenderly reaching out

in ways you may not see

but will feel

as surely as an embrace.

Positive Qualities Key Words:

balance

equilibrium

release

sexual wholeness

Love union

Problem Target Key Words:

blocked

stereotyped

sexual problems

negative images

The Balance of the Yin and Yang

The essence to restore equilibrium to the Sex/water chakra. To free the mind from masculine and feminine stereotypes and dogma. The union of Love between the male and female. For healing and restoring the balance to all aspects of female/male, Yin/Yang energy flows. To release blockages to these primal and vital flows. Also helpful in physical manifestations of these blockages such as restoring balance to the water element in the body as this essence basically re-harmonizes the sex/water chakra and related glands.

Mind - Common Uses:

Negative sexual imbalance can come about due to many influences. Unhealthy imagery of sexuality as a child, lack of healthy sexual definition from parents (who were undeveloped themselves), sexual trauma or distasteful experiences from childhood, early teens, or at any time in a person's life. This may lead to a freezing up, a desert or a flood tide of sexual expression.

People may react to the inner imbalance by focusing on sexuality out of proportion to other needs of their being, or by continually attracting the wrong sort of person to them, and thus perpetuate the negative emphasis in their minds. Self esteem and being able to trust anyone will suffer as a consequence.

A different direction for the unbalanced focus and negative development to take is brought about by the effect of rejection of strong sexual advances which leads to cruel and dominating behaviour.

For those who feel a sense of worthlessness because they do not feel complete in themselves.

For those with sexual problems such as frigidity and impotency.

For those with sexual inhibitions, or who find it hard to be open emotionally or sexually.

The healing brings about a balance of the primal states of Yin and Yang and manifests them into a wholeness of being. Any blocks are then dissolved and the Life enhancing energy can move through the person's being, and each of the feminine and masculine polarities and their forms in our being are enriched.

129

Physical - Common Uses:

Used for any imbalance related to the sexual organs and their functions.

Mind - Floral Acu-pressure

Psychological profile:
desire for isolation, aversion to people.
Uterus (seminal vesicle) acu-point on the ear. (see Pg 270)
Psychological profile:
confrontational, quick to respond in an aggressive manner to anything that seems threatening.
Adrenal acu-point of the ear. (see Pg 250)

Physical - Floral Acu-pressure

Physical symptoms:
 irregular menstruation, leucorrhoea, impotence, nocturnal emission.
Uterus (seminal vesicle) acu-point on the ear. (see Pg 270)
 (see also Cape Bluebell)
Physical symptoms:
hypotension, pulselessness, shock, asthma, inflammation.
Adrenal acu-point of the ear. (see Pg 250)
 (see also Ribbon Pea)
Physical symptoms:
impotency, sexual frigidity.
Genitalia (External) acu-point of the ear. (see Pg 254)
(used with the Macrozamia flower essence) (see also White Nymph and Purple Nymph Waterlily)
Physical symptoms:
painful areas on the muscles adjacent to spine, neck and joints.
Spinal, Neck and Joints acu-points on the ear.
(see Pgs 256-259, 265-266)
(see also Dampiera, Purple Flag Flower, Leafless Orchid, Menzies Banksia, Ursinia.)

Used topically for areas of the body that have swelling due to a build up of fluid. Used after surgery topically around (not on) a wound site.

Healing Pathway to the Soul

Each person has the forces of masculine and feminine within themselves. Each person is a symbol of the two great attracting opposites of Life. Two important lessons for human beings are; firstly that they must harmonize these forces within themselves and secondly they must harmonize the forces between the two sexes of human beings who share the planet. It is a great challenge to unify opposites, to see the complementary nature they hold for each other, to remember that it is only when harmony and a loving union exists that happiness is possible.

For spiritual liberation the higher union of Love between these two aspects within ourselves has to be achieved.

Meditation Poem

Macrozamia

My being is at one.

I receive my inner man and woman

my brother and sister.

Together they embrace

to fathom

the mysteries of Life.

Positive Qualities Key Words:

dedication

commitment

inspired

fulfilment

consistent

Problem Target Key Words:

irresponsible

run away

overwhelmed

freaked out

The Reliable Friend

The essence to calm, strengthen and inspire a person to face and deal with life and relationships so that stability and fulfilment come together at last. With new found consistency there is a deepening and maturing in all aspects of Life.

Mind - Common Uses:

For those with difficulties, such as panic and a need to run away when facing responsibility in relationships, work or family life or any area of life that requires responsible actions.
Used also where people have irrational responses to commitment or being consistent in their behaviour.

The healing settles the mind and brings in a sense of the Joy and interest in developing long term relationships and goals. The new consistency enables a greater fulfilment and an encouraging, positive response from people.

Mind - Floral Acu-pressure

Psychological profile:
feeling weak, wanting to pull away, can't cope, everything is too
much.
Stomach acu-point on the ear. (see Pg 267)

Physical - Floral Acu-pressure

Physical symptoms:
gastralgia, vomiting, dyspepsia.
Stomach acu-point on the ear. (see Pg 267)
(see also Blue Leschenaultia)

Healing Pathway to the Soul

True freedom of Spirit is when we can walk into any situation with
equipoise, dealing with any needs, any difficulties, in the same
loving way that we deal with pleasant surprises and fun. The calm
mind, enjoying being involved with Life is the one that can know
the deepest fulfilment.

Meditation Poem

Many Headed Dryandra

When I stand still

Life comes to me

bringing gifts of Love

and sometimes a load to be shared.

I accept with Joy

and nourish my Soul.

The Source of Love Eternal

The essence of the eternal Springs of Love. To inspire the realization that Love lies within and is important. To know Love is eternally with us and sometimes we taste it in the external world. For healing those who are holding in sadness and great hurt, this is the essence of finding higher Love.

Mind - Common Uses:

For those who have given love and have not received the same. This can be a child without tenderness from a parent, a parent without tenderness from a child or a lover without tenderness from a partner. The person to whom affections have been given may not be capable of returning such love and this the hurt giver finds hard to accept. They keep trying to get their needs met through the one person, or one type of person. They get sad, angry, frustrated, and even spiteful for they can't see why the person doesn't respond in kind. The depths of love these people long for are more surely found within the depths of themselves, where it can never leave them, or with a person who can truly appreciate their gifts.

The healing brings these people in touch with the deep core of their inner being where Love always resides. They are then more self assured and self contained, and feelings of hurt can heal.

Physical - Common Uses:

Used with Hybrid Pink Fairy Orchid for sensitive skin.

Healing Pathway to the Soul

The constantly changing scenery of Life and the ups and downs of people's desires, makes it painful for anyone who pins all their hopes of Love on other people. The knowledge of the Soul that Love is continually being rained down upon every one, a ceaseless flow of bliss for every individual being, is the reality to tap in to. All worldly love then comes as a bonus.

Meditation Poem

Mauve Melaleuca

Each moment

I am loved.

I am a lovable being

in a loving Universe.

I am full from the feast,

so deeply satisfied.

To Live Again

Positive Qualities
Key Words:

freeing

joyousness

healing

courage

regeneration

Problem Target
Key Words:

fear

trepidation

hesitation

pessimism

blocked

The essence of rebirth, of looking forward to tomorrow's experiences. To open to the strength of Joy which pain cannot touch. To move on through and past pain without fear and expectation of repetitions, without closing doors to Life. Especially in the realms of human relations, this fear and hesitation blocks joyful new beginnings. This essence encourages regeneration, renewal and courage, using painful experiences as an opportunity for greater depth and a source of determination to move forward.

Mind - Common Uses:

Painful experiences can form a barrier to future good experiences. If the painful experience is not healed then part of the person is caught in a time warp where that pain always exists. Every experience is then only seen through the distorted lens of the past. This means that one hurtful relationship will generate suspicion that hurt will come from every other relationship, that after a betrayal the person is distrustful of others. Being caught in this script blocks out new opportunities for happiness.
For the person caught up in their pain and not able to see beyond it. For those trying to transcend pain.

The healing brings regeneration to people, renewing Joy, wisdom and optimism that with what they have learnt, and with a healed heart, tomorrow will certainly bring more happiness. Their new depth of feeling enables them to walk through Life loving, yet fearless.

Physical - Common Uses:

Used topically around (not on) wound sites, and on painful areas where no skin is broken.

Physical - Floral Acu-pressure

Physical symptoms:
radiating painful areas on the muscles adjacent to spine and neck.
Painful areas on the muscles adjacent to spine, neck and joints.
Spinal, Neck and Joints acu-points on the ear.
(see Pg 256-259, 265-266)
(see also Dampiera, Purple Flag Flower, Leafless Orchid, Macrozamia, Ursinia.)

Healing Pathway to the Soul

The purpose of pain can be seen as a lesson, but for many it is a brick wall, a halt in their development as a human being. To use the holocaust as a means of regeneration and renewal is to conquer all negativity and claim the fearlessness and Joy within you as your birthright. The past then is truly past.

Meditation Poem

Menzies Banksia

The fire has been through me,

and into the ash

I throw the seeds for a new day.

I am reborn

from every branch I send out

new shoots and buds

to grow and blossom.

*Positive Qualities
Key Words:*

awareness

in touch

appreciation

perspective

*Problem Target
Key Words:*

complaining

burdened

isolated

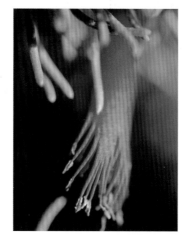

Awareness of the Collective

The essence of being in touch with the people around you, of being able to be aware and encouraging. For those who are feeling unsupported and overwhelmed, to help them re-focus on the contribution others are making, then sensitivity to other's problems and burdens is born. This awareness and empathy can serve to improve everyone's situation.

Mind - Common Uses:

For those feeling they are unfairly carrying everyone's workload on their own shoulders, such as people in leadership positions or situations such as being a single parent or self employed. They feel they are swamped by the demands of their life and lose perspective about how life is for everyone else.
For those feeling isolated due to what they perceive as lack of support from others.

The healing is to get back to a state of sensitivity towards others, regardless of one's own load. Invariably the perspective then becomes balanced and more opportunities open up for sharing responsibilities or being mutually supportive and encouraging.

Healing Pathway to the Soul

When we come from a personal perspective only, we miss the "big picture" of Life. All people are engaged in the processes of growth, challenge and the attaining of wisdom. To honour what other people are experiencing, and acknowledge their difficulties, means we can better assess what we are facing, and see what part we can play in the collective.

Meditation Poem

One-sided Bottlebrush

In the reflection of my day

I see the lives of others.

Some struggling, some flying,

some watching, some doing.

Empathy opens my eyes

to the paths of other's lives.

To Remain Tender

*Positive Qualities
Key Words:*

softness

tender

sensitive

compassion

*Problem Target
Key Words:*

hardened

gruff

intolerant

selfish

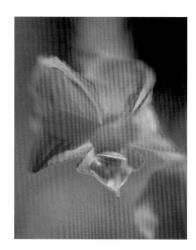

The essence of gentle perseverance and sustaining benevolence. Bringing one in touch with the softness of Life, empathy re-emerges. The hardened outer skin then becomes subtle and supple again, and is able to receive and give Love. For those who have been gradually closing up and desensitizing because of the harsher realities of Life and human relations.

Mind - Common Uses:

For people who have been through the school of hard knocks, a general desensitization occurs. Even when they are soft in their hearts they don't show it. People see only the rough exterior and may consider the person harsh. In reality they are wounded people with a Rhino skin to protect them. In spite of the Rhino skin they still get hurt, but other people will not realize it.
When seeing someone going through a hard time these people will say, "well I had to go through it, so you will have to as well". It is a typical reaction of some people in the older generations.

The healing opens the heart once more and regenerates tenderness and compassion for the lives of others, being able to show sincerely that caring and love are there for those who need it.

Healing Pathway to the Soul

When we harden up to get through the struggles of our journey we lose more and more Love from our experiences. The art is to be detached from the ups and downs, learning all the while, but never to distance ourselves from the sufferings of others, and, where we can, lend our encouragement. This creates an atmosphere around our lives of gentleness and Love.

Meditation Poem

Orange Leschenaultia

I can feel the rain and the sun,

the cold wind and the warm earth.

I sense all the beauty,

every vulnerable part.

I will shelter the fragile heart

and give it warmth.

Positive Qualities
Key Words:

expressive

articulate

calm

communicate

detached

Problem Target
Key Words:

hurt

explosive

uncontrolled

provoked

bottled up

The Articulation of Expression

The essence of detachment, considered words and actions. To enhance full expression, response and articulation of feelings without being angered or provoked. To inspire maintenance of internal good will, to let harsh words pass through you and not damage your equipoise. To stop and think, to come from a higher aspect in yourself before reacting in a way that could produce more hurt.

Mind - Common Uses:

For those who feel threatened by people who are mentally more agile than they are. Often these people feel frustrated with themselves and think of what to say after the person they were trying to communicate with is no longer there. If their short fall in articulating their feelings is used as an unfair advantage by others, feelings start to boil up inside them. If this builds up they can explode in self defence, having no recourse to words, perhaps even using physical force.

People who are easily taunted into aggressive behaviour, who overreact physically to verbal smart talk or cruelty, are often the people who find self expression difficult. This can be a child in the school yard who strikes out, a man or a woman in an unhappy relationship with pent up emotions.

For those who resort to violence when they have bottled up feelings and are very frustrated and angry.

For those who use their physical strength as a way of resolving conflict.

The healing helps one to articulate feelings in a positive way and be able to walk away from a verbal fight when the only purpose from the other person is to inflict a sense of inferiority or shame. One then learns the beauty of detachment and mastery of the Self.

142

Healing Pathway to the Soul

Emotions can be very powerful, especially when they are translated into physical actions. When a person has not reached full development of their powers of expression, and their emotions rule them, the situation is more likely to occur. To be at the mercy of the emotions is to be a prisoner to the past which has moulded your personality. You are then like a computer with set software giving the same reactions to the same keys being pushed. Turning to the Soul, to our deepest aspect of being, helps us to heal our past and be free of reactionary patterns of behaviour, to be able to respond spontaneously to Life, each response thus considered in the light of its own merits.

Meditation Poem

Orange Spiked Pea

I hear what you say

and my mind scans the light

of its meaning.

Here I am at peace

in the warmth of my inner being.

Positive Qualities
Key Words:

kindness

conscience

perspective

justice

Light

Problem Target
Key Words:

manipulative

arrogant

duplicity

deception

predatory

The Light of Conscience

The essence of awakening and purification of the heart. The essence of conscience. For those who get caught in rapacious, manipulative power playing for their own gain, losing sight of the reality of natural Karma where Life asserts justice. A person with raised consciousness sees the futility of what they are doing and the effects on others. As the light of conscience pierces the darkness a new person is born.

Mind - Common Uses:

The mind that prides itself on abilities to control and manipulate people is bound to have problems in relationships with others. Theirs is a particularly hard form of superiority complex which does not like to be thwarted. If someone escapes their game they pursue them ever more vigorously until they win, but in the process expose themselves, their duplicity and selfish aims.

The healing inspires the surfacing of their conscience, long since suppressed so they could have their own way. Realizations come readily then about the repulsiveness of their actions, and genuine sentiments of shame arise. They feel a sickening impact at the thought of the excitement they got out of the game they played. The mind can then see that such ambitions of exploitation are a waste of precious time when Life could be full of the beauty of love and friendship.

Mind - Floral Acu-pressure

Psychological profile:
desire to trap and overwhelm.
Mouth acu-point on the ear. (see Pg 262)
Psychological profile:
perpetrating sadism, hatred.
The Spleen acu-point of the ear. (see Pg 264)

Physical - Floral Acu-pressure

Physical symptoms:
facial paralysis, ulceration of the mouth.
Mouth acu-point on the ear. (see Pg 262)
(see also Leafless Orchid)
Physical symptoms:
abdominal distension.
The Spleen acu-point of the ear. (see Pg 264)
(used with Cape Bluebell) (see also Swan River Myrtle)

Healing Pathway to the Soul

Every action creates an equal reaction, this is the law of Karma. It is a natural flow which ensures balance and transformation in creation. Everything in the Cosmos is linked to everything else. One action vibrates waves that flow and bounce off other forms and lead to events. Anyone who thinks they are above this natural flow of the Universe will find out how real it is when the natural consequences of their actions come flowing back to them.

Meditation Poem

Pale Sundew

The Light is so intense

every part of my being

is accentuated and defined.

I am seen in total nowhere to hide

I am free and naked to Truth.

Positive Qualities
Key Words:

self esteem

assertive

dignity

inner strength

Problem Target
Key Words:

withdraw

unappreciated

work horse

compromising

To Assert Fairness

The essence of self esteem and assertiveness. For hard working people feeling increasingly lonely and sad because they are unappreciated and treated like a reliable workhorse. This essence restores the sense of self dignity and inner strength, not to withdraw, but to be actively part of society and able to assert one's rights as an individual.

Mind - Common Uses:

People who are dependable can be taken for granted, particularly when they are passive. Without appreciation and co-operation from others a sadness sets in and the person feels they just want to be alone and get on with their thankless life. Because they don't assert their rights the positive feed back they need for encouragement doesn't come. They walk away empty handed and disillusioned.

The healing inspires an ability to say no to those who try to use them, and not compromise their inner worth. Although conflicts can arise, they are a healthy re-balancing of energy, which helps the unhealthy situation turn into a positive one, where the person can be part of Life with full enthusiasm.

Healing Pathway to the Soul

Humility is often expressed as a weakness and bowing to strength rather than a benevolent strength which knows no compromise. To serve Life with humility and Love enhances every aspect of our being. This must be carefully distinguished from simply being a doormat and taking the line of least resistance. If we allow others to dominate us we are doing harm in allowing an unhealthy state to be continually fed. Our responsibility is to see that we, and others, are engaged in healthy interactions that increase Joy.

Meditation Poem

Parakeelya

There are a million thank you's

that sing out

it is great you are here!

Join us in our dance

arm in arm linked

lifting each other up

none shall fall.

Positive Qualities
Key Words:

open

exploring

accepting

discriminating

inquisitive

Problem Target
Key Words:

limited

dogmatic

closed

defensive

The Free and Open Mind

The essence of opening up to new concepts and ideas. To take the fear out of the unknown and untried. To understand the value of the different hues instead of only perceiving things in black and white. To feel the thrill of exploring another realm of thought. To inspire full acceptance of the beliefs of others without feeling unduly persuaded or influenced against one's better judgement.

Mind - Common Uses:

For those who are stuck in limiting perspectives on life, refusing to look beyond them, fear is the basis of their reactions, fear of the unknown, or the untried.

For those who feel they know what is right, and whoever disagrees is wrong.

For those who feel intimidated by the views of others and find themselves being automatically defensive and dogmatic.

For people caught in religious, political, scientific or esoteric dogma which prohibits forward movement.

For those who wish they could change their Life direction but find they are their own worst enemy, hesitating, continually fearful of stepping onto a new path.

For people who can't understand the younger generation. For parents who rely only on their own upbringing script to raise their children and then find it doesn't work.

For people who are frightened by their partner exploring different lifestyles.

The healing brings a sense of mental vigour to be open to and rigorously assess new ideas for their worth, and have the courage to implement them into their lives, if they are positive.

Healing Pathway to the Soul

Life can seem so storm-filled that we rush to any safe harbour and fear going out again. We make some sense of Life and then hold onto our precious concepts, threatened by any other concept that may erode its sense of reality and safety. Our safe harbour can turn suddenly into a "Pearl Harbour" where we find our concepts out of step with reality and we are overwhelmed. The middle way is to be prepared to keep our mind open to new developments and expansions in consciousness, and choose that which is the most Life giving and positive, be it an old realization or a new one.

Meditation Poem

Pin Cushion Hakea

Wrapped in arms of the bird of Truth

soaring over the stars

seeing all that is to be seen.

A caravan of colours

splashes my mind

gay and free.

Positive Qualities Key Words:

sustaining

responsive

replenishing

Problem Target Key Words:

empty

dry

unfulfilled

burnt out

The Springs of Eternal Sustenance

The essence of replenishment, of sustaining care, filling one's heart with inspiration. To restore the milk of human kindness to the hearts of those whose caring has run out because it was relying on the emotional response. This essence gets one in touch with the higher and richer internal source, beyond personal limitations of energy. Giving from the limitless inner being enriches oneself and others.

Mind - Common Uses:

For those who feel burnt out from handling other people's problems, they find they distance themselves, and avoid closeness.
For people who feel dry inside, empty and unable to give out.
For those who find their intellect can conceive of a person's problem but there is no feeling of compassion arising.
For those who develop relationships purely on the basis of their own needs. They don't consider the other person's needs, but are focused on how good the relationship will be for them. When their needs are no longer being met they feel dry and empty inside because they have failed to draw on the deep side of their Love nature which would also satisfy the deep needs of their partner. The relationship would then be mutually nurtured and sustained.

The healing brings a new depth to interactions with others, a way of being in touch with the core of a person from the core of one's own being, in other words a sensitivity without excessive emotional drain. The quality of giving then rises to a level which is totally sustainable, drawn from the deep well of one's Love nature.

Healing Pathway to the Soul

When caring and giving we should always ask ourselves, "how much of my motivation to do this comes from the fact that it makes me feel good?". If the buzz we get out of the giving is getting a result, or people's appreciation, or praise, or their emotional responses, then the giving is conditional and will have a limitation. One day, when faced with someone's cares and woes, the impact will not be the same and one day concern may disappear altogether. For a benevolent person this is a distressing turn of events. They know it is not right. Giving from the inner Self without any thought of any pay-back is the only way to give out and not burn out.

Meditation Poem

Pink Everlasting

The well within is overflowing

many come to drink.

The spring refreshes

and the travellers go on their way.

The spring of my Soul

replenishes itself

distributing happiness.

**Positive Qualities
Key Words:**

serenity

equipoise

inner peace

resilient

composure

**Problem Target
Key Words:**

reacting

disturbed

stressed

overwhelmed

nervy

Carrying Inner Peace

The essence of inner serenity, equipoise, and maintaining one's own strength in all situations. To calm the inner core, enabling a person to carry their inner peace with them and to be discerning as to what elements of the external world they will allow to activate their attention.

Mind - Common Uses:

For those stressed by environmental chaos or pressure. Helpful for those easily influenced and changed by noises, clamour or emotionally charged environments.
For those who tend to get caught in other people's panic or hysteria.
For those who are frustrated by their inability to maintain their "space" because the external surroundings impact on them too greatly.
For those with weak nerves who find their life stressful.

The healing strengthens the sense of the inner Self with its inner peace, allowing the person to pass through or be in different environments, both unassailed and discriminating as to which external stimuli are to be responded to.

Physical - Common Uses:

Used in cases of stress where the person can't maintain their composure because of environmental disharmony.

153

Mind - Floral Acu-pressure

Psychological profile:
overreacting to hectic, noise, clutter, other people's emotional states,
feeling of falling apart, unable to cope.
Shenmen acu-point on the ear. (see Pg 263)

Physical - Floral Acu-pressure

Physical symptoms:
stress, insomnia, dream disturbed sleep, inflammation, pain.
Shenmen acu-point on the ear.
(see also Hybrid Pink Fairy Orchid, Yellow Flag Flower, Purple Flag
Flower, Cowkicks, Pink Fountain Triggerplant, Reed Triggerplant and
Violet Butterfly)

Healing Pathway to the Soul

To maintain inner sanctity of the Self amidst the many distractions
that come our way is a very useful development. Everything around us
seems to clamour for attention when we don't have our inner being in
charge nor maintain a heightened sense of discrimination. This art of
carrying our inner peace with us, wherever we are, is part of truly
knowing our own strength, and maintaining it.

Meditation Poem

Pink Fairy Orchid

The sage sits in the forest
the animals come in curiosity,
the butterfly lights upon a resting hand,
leaves swirl around,
yet nothing disturbs the inner peace.

The Return of the Vital Force

sitive Qualities
Key Words:

restoring

vigour

reconnecting

vitality

Problem Target
Key Words:

exhausted

unable to cope

drained

lifeless

The essence of restoring the vital force to one's being, the fire Qi that sustains you, gives you vigour and physical stability. To re-ignite the vital flame and the return of dynamism to the point where one can take over this most essential responsibility. For the person who is losing the inner vitality which keeps one alive, either by a gradual draining on the physical level, or a cutting off in the subtle bodies.

Mind - Common Uses:

A lack of vital force. The feeling that energy is slowly draining away and not returning. In cases where people deny the needs of the physical body or a situation where the interfacing of the strength of their mind to their physical level is important and they can't manage it.

Physical - Common Uses:

For extreme tiredness or lethargy caused through ill health or shock to the body. Examples are surgical operations, weakness from viral infections and general convalescent situations. The essence rejuvenates our physical vital force.

Mind - Floral Acu-pressure

Psychological profile:
vital force has been neglected, underestimating the needs of the physical body.
Heart acu-point on the ear. (see Pg 255)
(see also Cowkicks, Purple Enamel Orchid, Reed Triggerplant)
Psychological profile:
feelings of falling apart unable to cope.
Shenmen acu-point on the ear. (see Pg 263)

Physical - Floral Acu-pressure

Physical symptoms:
unable to regain strength, overwhelmed by tiredness.
Heart acu-point on the ear. (see Pg 255)
(see also Cowkicks, Purple Enamel Orchid, Reed Triggerplant)
Physical symptoms:
insomnia, dream disturbed sleep, inflammation, pain.
Shenmen acu-point on the ear. (see Pg 263)
(see also Hybrid Pink Fairy Orchid, Yellow Flag Flower, Purple Flag Flower, Cowkicks, Reed Triggerplant, Violet Butterfly, see which combination or single flower applies to the situation)

Healing Pathway to the Soul

In the Yogic concept of Prama, balance between the physical, mind and spiritual levels, is essential for human existence. This triangle of states of being, when in harmonious development, gives the best foundation for the evolving of consciousness and the experience of fulfilment. To be a human being is a precious gift, for a human lives in all the levels of existence and can consciously create harmony between them all. So it is important to maintain the physical body in a healthy vital state where it will not let down the mind and the spiritual sides of our being and all can advance together.

Meditation Poem

Pink Fountain Triggerplant

I draw the internal fire

into the core of me.

The precious breath of Life

fans the embers

with energy.

I rise up in strength.

The Courage of the Lone Traveller

Positive Qualities
Key Words:

courage

prevail

inner strength

determination

Problem Target
Key Words:

compromised

overwhelmed

opposition

struggle

The essence for courageously standing by convictions of the heart. To be able to take the road you know is right, regardless of how others view your choices, maintaining the fight for one's morality amidst opposition. The inner strength to prevail without compromise even when the struggle seems long and potentially overwhelming.

Mind - Common Uses:

For the idealist who no longer stands up for their previously held ideals or standards due to lack of support.

For the person who has suffered when trying to live by their heartfelt convictions. Because of their personal standards they are forced to bear extra burdens and face greater struggle. When the sacrifice seems too great they start compromising their standards and lose determination.

For those who wish to be resilient in the face of opposition, when they feel like the "odd one out".

The healing brings the strength, creativity and courage to conquer this negative scenario, and the desire to retain working ideals and standards, no matter what obstacles arise.

Healing Pathway to the Soul

One of the ways that our inner realizations are brought out into the world is through the tests of compromise. Not to be rigid and unyielding in one sense, yet hold to the Truth we know inside, is a very conscious choice. When we feel our inner ideals are unsupported a slow erosion of these inner morals and wisdom can occur, and if it goes far enough we can lose sight of all the things which make Life beautiful. To nurture and feed the inner jewels of our highest ideals gives us the strength to go it alone, if necessary, fully satisfied by the beauty of the Path we take.

Meditation Poem

Pink Impatiens

The Truths I know so dearly

are woven into my being.

They are part of me.

They are my heart, my voice

and as I make my way

in company or alone

my song rings out.

Positive Qualities
Key Words:

focused

purposeful

achievement

mental vigour

Problem Target
Key Words:

vague

meandering

unconnected

unfocussed

Energy and Focus

The essence of strength of focus. To harness the inner strength of purpose and direct it towards important goals. Encourages achievement through new mental directness. Helpful for those who find difficulty in maintaining purpose, who feel they get lost half way through a thought process or activity. Excellent for attaining healing objectives.

Mind - Common Uses:

For the person who cannot follow their thoughts through, losing energy and focus and sometimes not realizing they have drifted away from and forgotten what they were setting out to achieve.
For those who get frustrated with themselves for not keeping "on the ball".
For those who feel bad about themselves because they feel their mind isn't strong enough to focus properly and achieve like others do.

The healing brings a centering and consolidation of the mind to an internal point. From this point the mind can maintain its vigour on the work or situation at hand until it is completed.

Mind - Floral Acu-pressure

Applied directly to the floral point four finger widths above the navel used for directing energy at childbirth when the mother is finding difficulty concentrating on working with the birthing process.

Physical - Floral Acu-pressure

For symptoms of losing track of a thought/study/objective.
Baihui acu-point on the head. (see Pg 272)

Healing Pathway to the Soul

There are many distractions for us as we seek to work through and work on the different aspects of our Life. When our internal strength is low it is far harder to maintain momentum, for the mind will lead us away to the external objects which dance in front of us demanding attention. It is so easy to be led away. It takes effort to stay on track, effort to stay focussed and fuel internal strength.

Meditation Poem

Pink Trumpet Flower

In the centre of the circle

I sit and contemplate.

I set my bearing

and with power

move forward in a straight line

wrapped in the glow of my inner being.

*Positive Qualities
Key Words:*

considerate

compassion

*Problem Target
Key Words:*

resentful

reactionary

hurt

hardening

To Rise Above the Self

The essence to take full responsibility of oneself to free and strengthen the heart. To not depend on and then react to people who let you down. In this way to become a truly helpful and understanding person, such as is needed by oneself, and others in the world every day.

Mind - Common Uses:

For dependency/resentment cycles where a person becomes hard after being let down and treated unfairly by other people.

For those who find they are becoming like the very people who have been inconsiderate or hurtful to them.

For people who lose sensitivity and compassion for others after bad experiences with those on whom they relied on.

The healing brings a sense (inner strength) of doing right by people, and being aware that they may not be capable of doing the same in return. In this awareness and positivity the situation will not occur where one becomes like the very people one resents.

Healing Pathway to the Soul

It can be a trap to focus on ourselves and what is our due. It can bring about inner weakness. Self pity is not positive, and it can create a focus on the negative traits in others. Not only can this distort our general perspective, but when focusing on negative traits our minds begin to mould into the shape of that negativity, we absorb it and start becoming the same. Keeping the mind above such things is not a process of denial or ignorance but a conscious effort to remain walking in the Light of our Spiritual Self, that is, in awareness and Love. From this inner strength we can be of great service to those who need understanding and compassion.

Meditation Poem

Pixie Mops

The endless wave of Joy

that comes

from the ocean within me

spreads outward

then rises up again, from the

peacefully deep. depths

eternal. Compassionate, understanding

Positive Qualities
Key Words:

openness

sensitivity

understanding

vulnerability

Problem Target
Key Words:

blaming

negative

arguing

criticizing

reacting

Holding Hands of Love

The essence to inspire a new perspective of understanding in a relationship, enhancing sensitivity and a positive approach to problems without blame. To seek mutual solutions that inspire trust and the forming of new aspects of Love.

Mind - Common Uses:

For those in relationship problems who cannot get past their reactions to the other person.

For those who can only discuss things by bickering and criticizing the other person.

For partners to drop the blame game and concentrate on sensitivity to the other person, thus allowing constructive rebuilding of trust and other solutions. Helpful for objective self analysis and rebalancing of partnerships with circular arguments of blame.

For parents or partners who are focused on their desires and ideals. They compound their own dissatisfaction because the less understanding they give their child or partner, the less positive responses they get, which in turn makes them feel justified in their self centred approach.

The healing ensures that the focus of the problem is in the centre and not put onto the other person. Being in touch with the other person and not focusing on winning a fight, or having their own way, many new possibilities arise to renew the relationship. Often both partners need to take the essence.

Used for bath therapy (with Red Leschenaultia).

164

Healing Pathway to the Soul

All problems between people need the sensitive approach, this means the ability to be in touch with how the other person feels, and what is needed for their journey. It is easy to get caught in the Ping Pong game of reactions. The ego does not want to submit, it wants to win, to feel satisfied with the other person being exposed as wrong. This in itself should ring a warning bell for a person wanting to move in a more spiritual direction. The little "i", the personality of the Self, clamouring for attention, always gets what it wants at the expense of the Soul. The Soul can come through in actions of selflessness and wisdom. We find that when we choose not to indulge the little "i", and allow Soul expression, problems have a way of becoming major leaps forward in human understanding.

Meditation Poem

Purple and Red Kangaroo Paw

Let us be together

our hearts full and calm.

Let us treasure each other

and open the jewel case

of the other's mind

in wonder.

Positive Qualities
Key Words:

consistent

confidence

regulating

stamina

achievement

Problem Target
Key Words:

up and down

collapsing

erratic

weak

To Master the Qi

The essence to instill consistency in achievement and energy output. To create a balance between work and rest. Helpful for those who do too little, then too much - and then collapse. The practical use of energy encourages better self esteem and confidence. Proving oneself is no longer an issue.

Mind - Common Uses:

For those who feel defeated, useless and are feeling unable to prove to others that they can reach a goal.
For those who feel they are not achieving enough and then "flog" themselves with work loads. Often the next phase is overload and breakdown.
For those who are in a regular cycle of having high energy and then falling apart.

The healing allows for control and proper use of the Qi for pursuits, i.e. the right amount of effort and then the regular release of pressure and the coming to rest. This maintains a line of activity and achievement without negative side effects of physical and mental deterioration.

Mind - Floral Acu-pressure

Psychological profile:
unrealistic and inconsistent with energy out-put.
Heart acu-point on the ear. (see Pg 255)

Physical - Floral Acu-pressure

Physical symptoms:
great highs and lows of energy, inability to sustain vitality with consistency.
Heart acu-point on the ear. (see Pg 255)
(see also Cowkicks, Reed Triggerplant, Pink Fountain Triggerplant,)

Healing Pathway to the Soul

Life is long - as long as it takes. To get to where we want to go, the line of energy involved must steadily progress with us. The energy must be stable and the phases of pause should best be measured, like a deep breath. Making sudden leaps forward is invigorating when they are sustained and disappointing and disillusioning when they melt away to nothing. As the mind is the projector of our Qi, our vital force, the mind must have consistency for the energy to be harnessed for our journey, for progress to be sure.

Meditation Poem

Purple Enamel Orchid

The seed at rest stirs to life

uncurling itself with leaf and branch

to reach the Sun and sky.

I breathe in the air I take in the Light

I rest on the earth.

Serenity

*Positive Qualities
Key Words:*

calm

diplomatic

balanced

settled

*Problem Target
Key Words:*

emotional messes

confusion

hopeless

The essence to gain and maintain serene objectivity amidst very personal issues of the heart that threaten to imbalance you. To feel calm and open to others when problems arise. This essence encourages objectivity without compromising richness of feeling and sensitivity towards loved ones, and is helpful in times of relationship upsets.

Mind - Common Uses:

For those who feel that human relations are a jungle full of unseen dangers and entanglements.
For people who become caught up in emotional storms in relationships and can not see what is really happening.
For those who prefer to cruise along, and conveniently ignore the intricacies of life. This attitude leaves these people susceptible to not seeing things in perspective.
For those wishing to come from a wiser space when dealing with knotty emotional problems.

The healing allows a calming of flaring emotional states. With a calm mind, that sees the different emotional states and where they come from, it is easier to deal with issues wisely. This essence helps one to see the implications of any actions or reactions, and understand the ins and outs of relationships, taking into account the details that create situations.

Mind - Floral Acu-pressure

Psychological profile:
looking for support from others, failing in one's own endeavours because there is no support from others. Feeling let down.
The Small Intestine acu-point of the ear. (see Pg 264)

168

Physical - Floral Acu-pressure

Physical symptoms:
Headache, vertigo.
Brain Stem acu-point of the ear. (see Pg 250)

Healing Pathway to the Soul

It is an achievement to be in touch with the world of feeling and still have the clarity of mind to perceive the intricacies involved in human relationships. Our emotional states can colour everything we see, can hide the truth from us. The mist of emotions creep in and tug at our insides. We then find it hard to know if our reactions are our own or triggered by someone else's emotions. To clam up tight in an effort to keep other's emotions outside will not sort out the problem, neither will immersing oneself in the sea of feelings. The way through is to be serene in the mind, aware and open to what others are going through. When someone sees beyond and through the mist, is able to see everything that has been hidden or which is not obvious, responding calmly and objectively, everyone has a chance of making it to the other side.

Meditation Poem

Purple Eremophila

The wind is blowing all around

everything is moving.

I am the sweet scent

that comes to all

refreshing and serene

bringing solutions and peace.

The Release

*Positive Qualities
Key Words:*

release

relief

unwind

relax

*Problem Target
Key Words:*

tense

pressure

stress

anxious

The essence of relief and release. To create a way for the build up of pressure and tension to escape, and allow healing and relaxation of body and mind. To enhance the unwinding process and to release the sense of having to react automatically tensely to situations.

Mind - Common Uses:

For those who feel rising stress and find themselves on the edge of a breakdown.
For those who can't find a way to unwind, or that normal relaxing activities no longer work.

The healing brings a releasing, like having a valve which regulates how much pressure is healthful, and letting go of whatever is not. The person is then not caught in the tense response to life situations.

Mind - Floral Acu-pressure

Psychological profile:
feeling of going mad, losing one's grip on the mind.
Shenmen acu-point on the ear. (see Pg 263)

Physical - Floral Acu-pressure

Physical symptoms:
stress, insomnia, dream disturbed sleep, inflammation, pain.
Shenmen acu-point on the ear. (see Pg 263)
(used with Yellow Flag Flower) (see also Hybrid Pink Fairy Orchid,
Pink Fairy Orchid, Yellow Flag Flower, Cowkicks, Pink Fountain
Triggerplant, Reed Triggerplant and Violet Butterfly)
Physical symptoms:
painful areas on the muscles adjacent to spine, neck and joints.
Spinal and Joints acu-points on the ear. (see Pg 256-259, 265-266)
(see also Dampiera, Menzies Banksia and Macrozamia)

Healing Pathway to the Soul

No matter how much pressure we build up and throw at our Life we
may not be able to move even a speck of dust. It is not the amount of
hectic we produce that makes things go right, that makes things
happen, but our general purposefulness and directness towards inner
goals. Some may try to keep ahead on their journey by staying tense
and ready for anything, but they are likely to blow out. Acceptance of
situations and working with them in an open way brings better all
round results.

Meditation Poem

Purple Flag Flower

My being is open

everything that was tight

is now so loose.

The breeze

swings me to sleep,

my sigh is deep.

Selfless Love

*Positive Qualities
Key Words:*

Selfless Love

heart

depth

impartial

freeing

*Problem Target
Key Words:*

emotional

frustration

hurt

unfulfilled

The essence to free the Spirit with unconditional Love. The essence of selfless service. To drink from the deeper side of one's Love nature. Not to be caught in emotional traps in dealings with fellow humans or your own Life path. To sensitize to a point beyond personalization, freeing the heart with service. Helpful for those who desire to merge with the Universal purpose and on all levels, practical and internal, share their treasures with others.

Mind - Common Uses:

For the person who can't differentiate between personal and impartial giving.

For those feeling hurt when not appreciated, needing to be able to handle people from a deeper perspective. Desire for fulfilment in personal relationships is thwarted and frustration, sadness and irritation set in. Often the person tries to change the one who is the object of their love to accommodate their desires and wishes but such a process can take an eternity and mostly it just doesn't work out.

For those who have jobs or activities centred around people, such as school teachers, nurses, therapists, parents, this essence inspires the giving of unconditional Love, that is Love with no strings attached, which allows the best outcome for those who receive and those who give.

For the spiritual aspirant.

The healing brings a sensitivity beyond the point of personalisation, thus freeing the heart with service and genuine Love. Such people then feel free to Love without concerning themselves for what response may occur in return, and so the atmosphere of Joy around them increases.

172

Mind - Floral Acu-pressure

Psychological profile:
over-sexual, strong desire for excitement and fun.
External Genitalia acu-point on the ear.. (see Pg 254)

Physical - Floral Acu-pressure

Physical symptoms:
impotence, sexual frigidity, impotence.
External Genitalia acu-point on the ear.. (see Pg 254)
(use with White Nymph Waterlily) (see also Macrozamia and Balga)

Healing Pathway to the Soul

The personality craves personal emotional fulfilment. This is natural.
Our journey through the wants of the personality to the wisdom of
seeking the peace of the Soul is a journey that teaches us where true
fulfilment lies. We find out that personal cravings demand a price,
binding us to the continual ups and downs of pleasure and pain.
When we respond from the Soul level we are completely free because
we are able to give and act without ties and conditions. We are not
moulding our responses to whether we get something in exchange.
The fulfilment lies in being able to give Love, in its many forms,
exactly as it is needed, - Selflessly.

Meditation Poem

Purple Nymph Waterlily

Cradled in the lap of Love

knowing that everything is

embedded with sweetness,

that the nectar flows through me

to every corner of the Universe.

Positive Qualities
Key Words:

at ease

social

interaction

balanced energy

Problem Target
Key Words:

discomfort

drained

hermit

unsettled

avoiding

The Sociable Spirit

To enjoy the company of fellows. The essence to transmute reservations about the demands of being social into a liberated social manner. Changing focus towards one's general internal direction ensuring a healthy flow of energy, and an ability to enjoy and deal with people without hesitation.

Mind - Common Uses:

For those whose perspective on friendship is what benefit they will reap from the association. What this means is that the focus is on weighing up the benefits rather than interacting freely with others. When they feel the ledger is tipping to their disadvantage they become uncomfortable with the friendship and want to withdraw.

For people who want to be in company but find that when they are, they wish they hadn't come at all. They feel too much is being taken from them, physically, emotionally or mentally .

For those who don't want to live alone but find it draining to live with another person.

For those who have been ill-used by people in the most simple social situations, they then feel unsettled when in company.

For feelings of restlessness, discomfort and tiredness that are accentuated in the company of others.

The healing brings an internal focus where the person maintains a social projection of themselves which is true to themselves and is assertive enough to establish a balanced rapport with others. There is then an energy balance not an energy drain.

174

Healing Pathway to the Soul

Humans are very socially engaged beings, in fact togetherness brings out the very best in us, and at times, the worst. It seems part of every human's journey to learn about other people and how to be amongst our fellows, able to give and receive without keeping a ledger. We cannot run away. We are part of humanity. We learn in our associations with others to maintain our journey and find at times the joy of company along the way.

Meditation Poem

Queensland Bottlebrush

Behind every face a story waits,

a person with a tale to tell.

Let me hear the stories of being alive

of knowing thorns and flowers.

I will tell of my own

and share our humanity.

Positive Qualities
Key Words:

true

Self revealing

open

depth

honest

Problem Target
Key Words:

masking

obligatory

shallow

image

insecure

The Unmasking of the Soul

The essence to find the true and deeper Self. Revealing and freeing for inner growth. To relieve the need to project anything other than what one truly is. Not to rely on external images and masks but to desire honest and meaningful connections to people. Frustration with shallow, empty and obligatory relationships is brought to an end by seeking the greater depth in the Self and other people.

Mind - Common Uses:

For those who rely on maintaining false or idealistic images of themselves to people so they will be liked and accepted, (i.e. insecurity)

For those who show whatever face people want to see to ensure their own personal advancement.

For the socialite who can only maintain superficial relationships.

Helpful with all types of psychotherapy and counselling to get past protective facades to the inner riches.

For those who wish to unmask their Soul and be true to themselves.

The healing takes away the fear of the consequences of just being who you are. It elevates the mind to a perspective from where a desire is born to be one with one's Self and to have the satisfaction of relationships with others where you are loved for your Self.

Mind - Floral Acu-pressure

Psychological profile:
easy, fun loving, lack of responsibility.
Gall Bladder/Pancrea acu-point on the ear. (see Pg 254)

Physical - Floral Acu-pressure

Physical symptoms:
pancreatitis, dyspepsia, diseases of bile duct
Gall Bladder/Pancreas acu-point on the ear. (see Pg 254)
(see also Reed Triggerplant)

Healing Pathway to the Soul

We learn from the time we are very young that people like a smiling face. Later we see how people respond to flattery or to being indulged in a conversation about themselves. From early on the masks start to be created behind which our true nature becomes hidden, - eventually even to ourselves. We can become unsure of what is the mask and what we have become on the inside. To let go of all the masks is to reveal the Self and allow it to have the consequences from Life which it needs to learn and grow. Masks limit our experience and interaction with Life which enhance our wisdom. To be truly at one with the Self, to know Self acceptance, is to know peace of mind.

Meditation Poem

Rabbit Orchid

I am what I am,

a traveller walking through Life.

All the riches of my being

are there for all to see.

177

*Positive Qualities
Key Words:*

in touch

patient

sensitive

closeness

attentive

*Problem Target
Key Words:*

absent

distracted

distant

restless

The Quality of Closeness

The essence of bringing one back in touch with loved ones on an enhanced level, promoting sensitivity. To be in the here and now, patiently, allowing time and space for closeness and the little joys of life together. To give of oneself in the moment of being close, with full attention and refinement of feeling.

Mind - Common Uses:

For those who are busy and find their mind strays when they are trying to spend quality time with loved ones. Subconsciously they feel that the interactions are a waste of time because they don't directly support their goals, desires and ambitions.
For those who are unaware of how out of touch they are with people close to them.
For working parents who find that a distance is growing between them and their children and/or their partners. They may be spending time with their family or partner but the absent mind means they are there in body only. Time goes by and distance increases.
People start not to rely on the relationship for fulfilment. People can easily end up as strangers living in the same house.

The healing restores the ability to focus the mind away from the comings and goings of the day and onto the moment in which closeness and relating is happening, to be able to "space out" with the ones you love. It develops the ability to be totally with a person and share the treasure of closeness.

Mind - Floral Acu-pressure

Psychological profile:
unfulfilled desires, a frustrated angry disposition.
Constipation acu-point on the ear. (see Pg 251)

Physical - Floral Acu-pressure

Physical symptoms:
constipation and/or diarrhoea.
Constipation acu-point on the ear. (see Pg 251)
(use with Red Beak Orchid) (see also Start's Spider Orchid)

Healing Pathway to the Soul

The mind races towards its personal goals and desires, expecting support and devaluing those people who don't support them directly. This devalued person can be one who simply wants to share Love with us. Just to BE is an art in life where the mind learns to sublimate its endless external plans and curiosities to the real experiences of the internal world. One of these internal delicacies that can easily be missed is the timeless communion with another Soul and all the sweetness of the combining of two hearts.

Meditation Poem

Red and Green Kangaroo Paw

There is no such thing as time

to the quiet heart

intimate with another.

Moments are treasured and rediscovered

in an endless warmth of feeling.

*Positive Qualities
Key Words:*

enthusiasm

resolve

responsible

desire

holistic

*Problem Target
Key Words:*

uninspired

lethargic

frustrated

rebellious

divided

Embracing Wholeness

The essence of renewing energy and inspiration to attend to all facets of life creatively and with equal enthusiasm. To be dynamic. To resolve the internal conflict between desire and duties, personal expression and responsibilities. To work on Life as a whole rather than separating it into antagonistic pieces.

Mind - Common Uses:

For those experiencing lethargy, listlessness and inability to get enthusiastic about their life.

For a problem with getting up in the morning, or sleeping too often during the day.

For adolescent and midlife dilemmas of rebellion or frustration about duties and family ties.

For those who cannot see how they can truly enjoy their life and maintain their job, family or other foundations of their life. They may resign themselves pessimistically or become hedonistic, because they can't see how they can attend to both directions simultaneously.

For those who fluctuate between being responsible and then totally neglecting their responsibilities.

For those suffering from burn out.

The healing resolves the conflict in the mind that our creative desires and wishes for fulfilment always have to be at odds with our relationships and other commitments. It brings the realization that one must use breadth of vision, creativity and good energy to make sure all parts of life are developing equally. The bringing together of the split energy-mind directions brings about a renewed zest for life and enthusiasm to work things out holistically.

Mind - Floral Acu-pressure

Psychological profile: unfulfilled desires, a frustrated angry disposition.
Constipation acu-point on the ear. (see Pg 251)
Psychological profile:
unmotivated, lazy.
Large Intestine acu-point on the ear. (see Pg 260)
Psychological profile:
can't care about things, drifting along.
Eye acu-point of the ear. (see Pg 253)

Physical - Floral Acu-pressure

Physical symptoms:
constipation and/or diarrhoea.
Constipation acu-point on the ear. (see Pg 251)
(used with Red and Green Kangaroo Paw and Start's Spider Orchid)
Physical symptoms:
constipation and/or diarrhoea.
(see also Start's Spider Orchid, Red and Green Kangaroo Paw)
Large Intestine acu-point on the ear. (see Pg 260)
Physical symptoms:
Eye diseases eye strain, problems focussing.
Eye acu-point of the ear. (see Pg 253)

Healing Pathway to the Soul

Any road is a very hard road to walk when we are in two minds about where we are going. So many aspects of our being can be calling out for desires to be fulfilled in different ways. To integrate ourselves as a whole all desires can be channelled into one major direction. This can be done without causing damage to ourselves or others when the direction is a spiritual one, because spiritual means all aspects are developed in harmony. This process brings us the boon of always looking forward to Life's experiences and having a mind full of vigour and optimism.

Meditation Poem

Red Beak Orchid

I am the gardener of my Life

appreciating and tending to all.

Every part of my life is watered

from the springs of my Soul.

*Positive Qualities
Key Words:*

helpful

sharing

supportive

enthusiasm

energy

*Problem Target
Key Words:*

lazy

burdening

isolated

rebellious

resentful

The Spirit of Helpfulness

The Joy of being fully part of a combined effort. To know the Joy of achieving together. To help a person rely on their own energy and be aware of sharing burdens in family and community life. The return of this energy flow then sees a general boost to overall energy output and creativity in all areas of the person's endeavour.

Mind - Common Uses:

For those who feel they are on the outside of group activities. This is due to others feeling they are a "dead weight".

For those who have not realized the fact that all people working together to their best capacity makes a better life for everyone.

For adolescents who feel they should be provided for, whether or not they contribute anything.

For those who don't feel like doing their share of the work, and who are resentful when this fact is brought to their attention.

For those who focus exclusively on how they are feeling and not on how much they are burdening others by their lack of output.

For problems of laziness, free-loading.

The healing brings a realization that other people have gone through a lot of blood, sweat and tears to bring about what they have in life. The person then looks at their share of the work differently, with a sense of fairness. Instead of resenting other people for being frustrated with them, they see the response as natural and fair. From this point they can learn the joys of working together equally and in harmony with the collective.

Healing Pathway to the Soul

Every being holds up their little part of the Universe. When someone is taking energy unfairly from others it effects the Whole, and the Universe will create a reaction to correct the problem. This is unpleasant to experience. Far better to engage in Life fully and wholeheartedly, and in so doing discover the truth that there is an endless flow of energy for us to tap into any time when we are acting as part of the Whole.

Meditation Poem

Red Feather Flower

To reach above

and find a helping hand.

To look below and lift a person up.

Together we are strong,

each with the vigour

to be there for each other.

The Merging of Souls

Positive Qualities Key Words:

sensitize

melting

bliss

Love

closeness

gentility

The essence of gentleness and sensitivity, of experiencing bliss in relationships. To re-open the heart, engendering empathy with the struggles of others which then becomes an opportunity for openness and merging of Souls. Helpful to bring sweetness back to relationships, when harshness and brittle attitudes are stopping Love, Joy and closeness of life together.

Problem Target Key Words:

cold

harsh

uncaring

closed

contempt for

weakness

Mind - Common Uses:

For those who have become hardened because in the distant past they have come to the conclusion this is the only way to survive. They cut out and deny all sensitivities towards others.

For those who wish to know true intimacy with another, who find it hard to open up to affection.

For those who find that the hardness of the workaday world is becoming part of them and is stopping sweet spaces between them and their loved ones.

For working couples who can't leave the world at the door when they come home, and want to be left alone.

For those who have become harsh and uncaring, even beginning to despise the weaknesses of others.

For those who lose empathy and care only for themselves. Those who have contempt for weakness.

This essence is excellent for couples to use in a Bath therapy.

The healing activates the desire to Love and give sweetness, and a desire for the beautiful subtleties of intimate relationships.
It dissolves the hardness and enables deep trust and closeness, with exquisite sensitivity.

Mind - Floral Acu-pressure

Psychological symptoms:
feeling self sufficient, not needing anyone, not wanting to share with others.
Duodenum acu-point of the ear. (see Pg 252)

Physical - Floral Acu-pressure

Physical symptoms:
Duodenal ulcer, pylorospasm
Duodenum acu-point of the ear. (see Pg 252)
(see also Hybrid Pink Fairy Orchid).

Healing Pathway to the Soul

What a treasure it is to have a deep and sweet relationship with another person, to be completely open to giving and receiving Love, to know a sacred trust. This is a spiritual experience, a small reflection of the Great Oneness that is the true nature of all Life. When two people can be deeply open to each other it is an inspiration for all, showing how one day all humanity can enjoy such loving Oneness.

Meditation Poem

Red Leschenaultia

The melting of my armour

leaves me warm and secure.

Only love can embrace me now.

My soft skin can feel

every joyous touch of Life.

The Rejuvenation

Positive Qualities Key Words:

rejuvenate

restore

withstand

revitalize

recover

Problem Target Key Words:

struggle

exhausted

worn down

depleted

not coping

The essence to recharge after a long struggle. To bring back the feeling of wholeness of being where one's integral self is restored. To heal and then integrate and revitalize the parts of the mind and body that feel worn down. To restore inner strength, unify the mind and regain the ability to withstand the rigours of one's life.

Mind - Common Uses:

For the person who has never recovered their strength after an accumulation of hardships.

For feelings of anxiety, losing one's memory, feelings of instability. Being unable to cope with life in general.

For situations when a person, with the accumulation of all the experiences of life which were bruising, hurtful or traumatic, feels unstable and unable to cope. They become more and more fragile and anxious about their life situation.

A person who has lost connection to many parts of their being due to hurt or trauma will find it more and more difficult to function as time goes on. Even after an immediate trauma they can feel disjointed and almost out of touch with reality. They may not realize that it is the build-up effect that is really devastating them now.

The healing helps bring back the feeling of wholeness of being, where one's integral Self is restored, integrating and revitalizing the parts of the mind that are full of trauma, and therefore being kept isolated in the mind to prevent further trauma. Once the person feels their inner strength restored, the mind is unified and has the inherent ability to withstand the thrusts and parries of life and can go forward.

187

Mind - Floral Acu-pressure

Psychological profile:
insomnia, dream disturbed sleep, feeling of falling apart, unable to cope.
Shenmen acu-point of the ear. (see Pg 263)
Psychological profile:
oversensitive, inability to stand up for oneself, weakness.
Gall Bladder/Pancreas acu-point of the ear. (see Pg 254)

Physical - Floral Acu-pressure

Physical symptoms:
lack of energy after a series of traumas, perhaps over a long period of time.
The Heart acu-point of the ear. (see Pg 255)
(see also Cowkicks, Pink Fountain Triggerplant, Purple Enamel Orchid)
Physical symptoms:
insomnia, dream disturbed sleep, inflammation, pain.
Shenmen acu-point of the ear. (see Pg 263)
(can be used with Pink Fairy Orchid, Hybrid Pink Fairy Orchid, Cowkicks, Pink Fountain Triggerplant, Violet Butterfly) (see also Purple Flag Flower and Yellow Flag Flower)
Physical symptoms:
pancreatitis, dyspepsia, diseases of bile duct
Gall Bladder/Pancreas acu-point of the ear. (see Pg 254)
(see also Rabbit Orchid)

Healing Pathway to the Soul

Resilience is a feature of human beings. One can always be amazed at what amount of adversity we can experience, and be devastated by, and yet still hold on to Life. A long and continual battle of this nature can only be survived with the continual healing of the inner Self and its very vitality. We must also face the reason why these events are repeated, and what is the lesson we are not learning thereby prolonging our agony.

Meditation Poem

Reed Triggerplant

Standing beneath the fountain

splashed in sunlight

bathed till I am new

refreshed and free.

Every part of me alive.

*Positive Qualities
Key Words:*

fearless

calm

accepting

positive

*Problem Target
Key Words:*

foreboding

dread

anxiety

fear

Safe Within the Universe

The essence of fearlessness. To feel the safety of Being. To rise above fear and foreboding that stops positive attitudes and directions that are desired for a fulfilling life. To dissolve the feelings of nameless dread, panic or fear of death.

Mind - Common Uses:

For those who feel overwhelmed in a situation and want to flee.
For a person responding fearfully to a supposed or real threat.
The person facing traumatic surgery.
The refugee who has seen much death and destruction.
A person facing thoughts of the reality of death after experiencing someone dying.
A person feeling intense fear and anxiety.
This essence is for the fear of the unknown, fear of annihilation and what might happen to oneself.

The healing takes away the fear and brings a realization of how destructive and unnecessary it is. The situation can then be faced fearlessly. As irrational or as logical as the fear may seem to be, one must be in touch with the realities of Life and living which are the real challenges. By halting the fear response one can regain composure and go forward.

Mind - Floral Acu-pressure

Psychological profile:
impulsive, panicky.
Adrenal acu-point of the ear. (see Pg 250)

Physical - Floral Acu-pressure

Physical symptoms:
hypotension, pulselessness, shock, asthma, inflammation.
Adrenal acu-point of the ear. (see Pg 250)
(see also Macrozamia) .

Healing Pathway to the Soul

There is only transformation in this Universe. There is no end. Every Pathway goes on to the next place of renewal. When we were young we lost one baby body and got an adolescent one, then we lost that to take up the adult one. We can lose so many different forms and mind states to transcend to others in one lifetime let alone many lifetimes. Fear brings us nothing but a distraction to our challenges in Life, and takes us far from the sweet experience of our eternal Soul.

Meditation Poem

Ribbon Pea

My Spirit is indestructible, timeless and has travelled

through time and space.

I am tested that I may become strong.

I enjoy uncertainty,

I welcome the unknown

invincible I stand.

The Inner Quiet

Positive Qualities
Key Words:

peace

tranquillity

inner quiet

at ease

**Problem Target
Key Words:**

tense

stressed

edgy

disturbed

hassled

The essence of being able to hold an inner place of stillness, peace and tranquillity. To be able to ease the mind at any time in any place. To maintain sweetness and equanimity of mind inside, and not wait for perfect surroundings in which to feel at ease.

Mind - Common Uses:

For those who wish to maintain their equilibrium when living with other people.

For parents who feel tense when the children are around them.

For those who feel the need to escape to their own "space" continually as a way of relieving tension. (This is not a permanent solution)

For those who become edgy, uptight and easily disturbed.

For those in people professions.

The healing brings the person in touch with a "space" inside themselves that can remain at peace regardless of external happenings. This helps to engender a calm atmosphere in the general surroundings, and other people can positively respond to it.

Physical - Floral Acu-pressure

Physical symptoms:
morning sickness (during early pregnancy) , nausea.
Use on the navel, just a couple of drops of essence every few hours.
(use also with Black Kangaroo Paw on the same point)

Healing Pathway to the Soul

Peace is always within and can be sent out into the world where it can nourish and heal. To rely on the world to provide a peaceful environment for us is to know frustration. To rely on developing our inner room of quiet means a lasting and life-long positive experience.

Meditation Poem

Rosecone Flower

At peace amongst the bustle

slow amidst the rush

thoughts rise and fall

on my inner lake

within always a hush.

Positive Qualities Key Words:

break through

dynamism

inspired

free to express

Problem Target Key Words:

oppressed

powerless

unresolved

obstructed

To Break Through

To become free to move forward. The focus of spiritual energies that will consistently break up negative oppressive forces in the environment. The essence to give a sense of protection and dynamism where powerlessness has previously prevailed. A deep internally inspiring and extremely subtle flower essence which is of great benefit to those dedicated to the Path of Light.

Mind - Common Uses:

For those who are trying to establish new ideas.

For those who feel they have become powerless to change a situation.

For those feeling unable to express themselves freely within their life, there seems to be an invisible force stopping them.

For situations where pressing issues need to be resolved that have no clear solutions. The tendency is to put problems in the background of our life. This creates two types of problems, one is that the problems still subconsciously affect us and make it hard to really relax. The other is we become less consciously aware of the problem so a solution becomes more illusive.

This healing is like a protective cocoon, like a mother's womb wherein one can recover and find strength and peace. It stimulates a calm acceptance of the problem. It allows one to get on with life without being effected by the issue and when life offers a part or total solution to the problem, one's awareness and focus is there to perceive its worth and utilize it. The break through is then sure to come about.

Physical - Common Uses:

Used in spray therapy around places where a virus (for example influenza) is likely to take hold.

Healing Pathway to the Soul

At times when we are making progress and working positively in Life it seems that an opposing wind tries to stop us. To break up old structures and build new ones is a great task needing a high degree of consistency, focus and vigour. Patience is also of enormous value, and the awareness of knowing that there are benevolent forces that come to our aid when the time is right, and that when all these aspects are in hand and the break through to a new day is assured.

Meditation Poem

Shy Blue Orchid

The way is clear

the road is straight

my mind at one

with the forces of goodwill.

Dawn approaches

I can hear it singing.

Positive Qualities
Key Words:

challenge

overcoming

mastering

persistence

Problem Target
Key Words:

giving up

stagnancy

rebellious

frustrated

The Spirit of Perseverance

The inspiration to tackle difficulties with the development of inner strength. To continually challenge oneself to overcome internal and external obstacles to progress. To never give up and say it is too much. To keep learning how to work something out until it is mastered.

Mind - Common Uses:

To help the mastering of a skill or aspect of learning.
To help establish healthy disciplines. Assists ending unhealthy addictions.
For those who give up too easily when a problem arises.
For those who don't achieve goals because they let small things get in their way.
For lack of persistence.
For those who try hard to improve but find the external obstacles overwhelming and then rebel.
For those who are frustrated with themselves because of stagnancy.
For students who feel they are in a learning dead-end.
For adolescents who try to do the right thing and then give up, become self destructive and rebel when someone is trying to help them through an obstacle to their happiness or success.

The healing brings a new resolve to tackle difficulties. With persistence comes the rewards that teach the person how the strength of their desire to achieve will ensure success.

Healing Pathway to the Soul

Every internal challenge we take to improve ourselves brings into focus how much inner strength we have. To admit defeat at any time is to stay still and continually experience frustration and a feeling of stagnancy. There are many ways to climb over a wall, and all ways might not end in success, but with perseverance a way will inevitably be found, and beyond the wall is our destiny.

Meditation Poem

Silver Princess

Hills and valleys

are the same

when using the wings of desire

and the strength of my heart

to fly beyond

the reach of gravity.

Positive Qualities
Key Words:

fulfilled

inner contentment

independent

Self Love

Problem Target
Key Words:

needy

hurt

bitterness

submissive

demanding

The Simplicity of Love

The essence of giving simple, deep and fulfilling Love. To encourage Self appreciation and an attitude in giving to others which brings about an emotional independence and contentment. Feelings of being needy subside and are transformed into caring from a Self assured centre.

Mind - Common Uses:

For those disillusioned by the lack of appreciation from others who they have loved.

For those who are motivated to love someone by their need to be loved, not by the individual qualities of the person they are attached to.

For those who keep giving to those who don't appreciate them.

For attachments to people based on a needy emotional imbalance.

For feelings of bitterness from not understanding why relationships go wrong.

For those who tend to be the submissive yet demanding partner in a relationship.

The healing brings an inner contentment and Self appreciation which inspires emotional independence in a positive way. One then gives where the giving is appreciated.

198

Healing Pathway to the Soul

To give Love where it is not valued or nurtured is throwing away the treasures of the heart. It does no one good and in fact can keep a relationship between people unhealthy. Wisdom in giving Love creates more Love and a better world.

Meditation Poem

Snakebush

Giving and seeing

a heart filled with Joy

illumines us all

and creates a gift

of lasting beauty.

*Positive Qualities
Key Words:*

optimism

confidence

positivity

encouragement

*Problem Target
Key Words:*

undermined

attacked

sad

uneasy

struggling

The Encouragement

The essence of belief in and optimism about ourselves and our direction. To bring back confidence and appreciation of our achievements even when all around is malice and doubt. To have renewed vitality in goals and objectives making it possible to move out of the sphere of influence of negative projections into the free space of positivity and success.

Mind - Common Uses:

To re-affirm self worth and confidence when another person is projecting negativity, whether psychically, in the form of gossip, or veiled malice.

To bring back forward momentum when others have sown the seeds of self doubt.

For a person who is the target of negativity and finds they are losing vitality.

For people who are being undermined, often behind their back, and are losing confidence.

For uneasy feelings when dealing with people and one is not fully aware of their motives.

Those who trust people only to find they are abused, and information they have given is used against them.

The healing brings self confidence and a belief in one's direction. One then works positively on the way forward and is not waylaid by doubt.

Healing Pathway to the Soul

Optimism and confidence energize us and brighten our mind. These positive feelings about ourselves only last, and can stand up to the test of negativity from others, when they are based on deep beliefs of the inner Self. Anything that comes from more superficial parts of us is easily assailable and often crumbles under pressure. The invincible optimism and confidence comes from knowing the Self so well and directing our activities from the noblest states of mind which we can wholeheartedly embrace.

Meditation Poem

Snake Vine

I feel the smile within my mind,

it tells me to dance along,

enjoy the road,

keep my eyes towards the Sun,

and give no thought to shadows.

*Positive Qualities
Key Words:*

understanding

aware

accepting

empathy

wisdom

*Problem Target
Key Words:*

judgmental

inexperienced

condemning

short sighted

The Wisdom of Empathy

The essence of understanding the lives of others. To enhance empathy, to help one get in touch with how life is experienced by others, to integrate this into one's comprehension of Life. To view Life from a perspective that encompasses all the possibilities a person can face, and thus lose any judgemental attitudes. To inspire the realization that "one day this could happen to me" and so prepare oneself for the twists and turns that Life may present.

Mind - Common Uses:

For those who are naive about Life because of lack of experience, or lack of sharing the experiences of others.

For those who can't develop deeper relationships because they easily make shallow and sweeping judgements of other people's situations. For those who have not developed empathy and remain aloof from others.

For those who find themselves in a trauma and are unable to cope because of lack of experience of such things. Often they have never contemplated their life going amiss, or have not ever empathized with those who have had problems. Usually they condemned a person for being to blame for their own troubles. When they eventually meet difficulties they feel totally lost because there is no wisdom to draw on with which to face their plight.

The healing brings the person back in touch with people, being able to hold a much broader and wiser perspective, and being willing and open to learn about how it is to walk in another's shoes. This is how we learn about, and prepare for, the many twists and turns in our own life, with the added bonus of being able to share with our fellow travellers our joys and sorrows, and know comradeship.

Healing Pathway to the Soul

The illusion that there are set formulas to solve the problems of living, keeps people apart from each other and is unhealthy for society. It is unhealthy because all people have the same basic want, that is to feel Joy, and are going through the same processes of Life's lessons, in their unique and individual way. The collective wisdom of humanity about how best to pass quickly through difficulties and on to Joy develops further with every era. If we separate ourselves from each other's experiences, are not able to weep and laugh together, and separate ourselves from collective learning experiences, then we inhibit the growth of social wisdom.

Meditation Poem

Southern Cross

When your heart cries

I feel it.

When you laugh

I smile.

Thank you my friend

for sharing Life with me.

*Positive Qualities
Key Words:*

perspective

decentralizing

Selfless

appreciating

*Problem Target
Key Words:*

focus on self

engrossed

fixated

The Panoramic View

The essence of the Selfless perspective where a true understanding of the individual's place in the scheme of Life is understood. To inspire an outlook where one's personal concerns don't have to be prominent and override all other concerns. The decentralizing of one's focus brings one in touch with the beauty and Joy that surrounds all Life and it can be appreciated anew.

Mind - Common Uses:

For those who wish to move towards a more spiritual and selfless state.

For the person in a central position in a family, group or organization who feels they are indispensable. Often they are pivotal to the workings of the collective and this can start giving them a false perspective on the importance of their personal needs.

For feelings of frustration with situations not turning out as one wants them to. Continually talking about one's own problems.

For people who are overly focused on their own feelings and needs. This focus is insatiable, they feel they have certain needs to be fulfilled before they will have contentment. It is an illusion, which drives them on, and there is never enough to slate their needy thirst. In the process the "I" centred attitude prevents both a sense of peace and inner tranquillity, and also the ability to lose the "self" and be at one with Life.

This healing decentralizes one's focus which brings one in touch with the beauty and Joy that surrounds all Life, appreciating it anew   -
this is the true fulfilment.

Healing Pathway to the Soul

When the personality gets attention, it very easily inflates and becomes distracted by its size. The Soul perspective is then lost, often leading to Life's lessons in Self importance and the true place of the little "i" in the wider Cosmic play. This can be so even when the person is involved in service to others and holds strong spiritual objectives. The way one personalizes the attention and respect from others can become a subtle test as to the true depth of one's spiritual nature.

Meditation Poem

Spirit Faces

Beyond myself I see the Light

of a thousand lamps

rending the night.

Each lamp illumines a face,

a precious link in the golden chain. of Life.

Positive Qualities
Key Words:

resolutions

creativity

open mind

hope

opportunities

Problem Target
Key Words:

blocked

hopelessness

blank

no options

tunnel vision

Creative Solutions

The essence of opening the mind to creative solutions and breaking out into new thought. To bring the realization and mental force to break into the realms of infinite options and choices which have always been there. With the new creativity and hope, life situations are completely turned around.

Mind - Common Uses:

For people wanting to find a way out of a seemingly impossible situation.

For those who feel there is no way out of their dilemma, that they are facing locked doors on all sides. They have lost hope.

For those who feel they have no options except the ones they don't like.

For artists and writers with a creative block.

For those who can't find the initiative to change their situation.

The healing brings a full opening of the mind to the myriad possibilities of action and choice that are always there in every situation. Helps the utilization of right brain decision making.

Healing Pathway to the Soul

The Universe is full of opportunities, of options and choices for what we can do and how we can do it. Habit of thought and sticking to well worn tracks in our minds leaves us oblivious to the bountiful assets that are all around, usually right in front of our noses. When facing a dilemma the mind can tend to become more constricted in its considerations. The creative flows are then frozen and blocked and everything can seem impossible. Nothing is impossible when we tap into the Universal mind.

Meditation Poem

Star of Bethlehem

Resigned, frustrated, my lot in Life.

Seeing me you sang

and revealed within me

the value of creative solutions.

Now I move on.

Thank You.

Positive Qualities
Key Words:

directness

courage

decisive

resolving

Problem Target
Key Words:

compromised

avoiding

messy

unclear

frustrating

The Direct Approach

The essence of directness and straightforwardness. Learning to deal with difficult people and situations in a benevolent but successful manner. To stimulate the mind to focus on what is real and important, bringing out the courage within to cut through emotional smoke screens in communications with people.

Mind - Common Uses:

Dealing with people who think they have the power in a situation to take advantage of you. Dealing with messy situations.
For those being too sensitive to the consequences of confronting someone who is dealing dishonestly with them or taking advantage of them, compromising the truth because of someone's power over them.
For those who accommodate burdensome emotional attachments that are on a road to nowhere.
For those wanting peace and therefore not dealing with difficult issues in a straightforward manner.

This healing essence enables a person to be direct and straightforward when dealing with difficult people and situations. Fearless of consequences, one refuses to accommodate the unfairness or game playing of others. Free from the muddy waters of indecision and unhealthy sentimental attachments, the results are often clarity between people, and a learning process for those who have not been clear and objective.

Mind - Floral Acu-pressure

Psychological profile:
dependency.
Cardiac Orifice acu-point of the ear. (see Pg 251)
Psychological profile:
energy and drive to fulfil one's desires, no energy to fulfil one's
responsibilities.
Constipation acu-point on the ear (see Pg 251)
Psychological profile:
desire to be left in peace, lethargic.
Large Intestine acu-point on the ear (see Pg 260)

Physical - Floral Acu-pressure

Physical symptoms: nausea, vomiting.
Cardiac Orifice acu-point of the ear. (see Pg 251)
 (see also Balga)
Physical symptoms: constipation and/or diarrhoea.
Constipation acu-point on the ear (see Pg 251)
(use with Red Beak Orchid) (see also Red and Green Kangaroo Paw)
Physical symptoms: constipation and/or diarrhoea.
Large Intestine acu-point on the ear (see Pg 260)
(see also Red and Green Kangaroo Paw, Red Beak Orchid)

Healing Pathway to the Soul

To be benevolent can mean many things. Benevolence is not always the soft and gentle course of action. It can be the most stormy course of all. The intent we have when dealing with people is the key. When we come from a sincere and selfless perspective, with no hidden agendas or judgements, then we will do the best for a given situation. This takes a resilient and a fearless approach, especially when dealing with people who are not fair or honest, or are playing with you for their own sport. It is good to remember that by indulging them in their game, in the name of nicety, we empower them to do the same to the next person, and so perpetuate the problem and their Karma.

Meditation Poem

Start's Spider Orchid

A generous heart

prepared to love.

Courageous and wise

prepared to listen.

Direct and definite

to deal with trouble.

The Spirit of Fairness

**Positive Qualities
Key Words:**

fairness

inner strength

positivity

insight

**Problem Target
Key Words:**

victim of

unfairness

or unfair person

self pity or

self justifying

suffering injustice

or

*perpetrator of
injustice*

The essence to manifest a non-compromising attitude towards fairness both within ourselves and from others. To inspire inner strength not to get emotionally caught when someone is unfair. To not accommodate another's unfairness and so avoid being taken for granted - this puts the responsibility on to the other person to examine their behaviour.

Mind - Common Uses:

For a person who is innocent to some of the harsh realities of life. A person who is suffering injustice and is unclear or unable to deal with the situation.

For great frustration and feelings of being tricked.

or

For a person on the other side of these situations who doesn't care whether they are fair or not to others.

For a person on the other side i.e. the perpetrator of unfairness, with symptoms of justifying unfair behaviour, perhaps with injustices done to them previously.

The healing brings a healthy sense of fairness on both sides of an unfair situation. Those who have suffered injustices and are feeling emotionally traumatized can distance themselves from the people involved. Now clear sighted, they get on with their own life with positivity, feeling healed and strengthened. Those who have ceased to be concerned about whether or not they are being fair regain this important attribute, and begin to care how everyone is placed in a situation.

Mind - Floral Acu-pressure

Psychological profile:
abused, hurt, a victim of injustice, sadism.
Spleen acu-point of the ear. (see Pg 264)
(see also Cape Bluebell and Pale Sundew)

Physical - Floral Acu-pressure

Physical symptoms:
abdominal distension.
Spleen acu-point of the ear. (see Pg 264)
(see also Cape Bluebell and Pale Sundew)

Healing Pathway to the Soul

When injustice seems to prevail it can provoke a rebellious feeling of "why then, should I be fair?". When in a position that seems unfair, the challenge is to see what we can change about ourselves and our position so that there will be an improvement. Sometimes this will mean having the inner determination to walk away from the situation and get on with our greater goals instead of continually compromising them in an unhealthy set of circumstances.

Meditation Poem

Swan River Myrtle

Be prepared to go

to wherever good things thrive and grow.

An inner guide whispers the way

to where impartiality and decency

prevail.

The Joy of Self Worth

Positive Qualities
Key Words:

happy

Self appreciation

Self worth

Problem Target
Key Words:

inferiority

victim

sad

down trodden

The essence of positive appreciation of one's internal gifts and potentials to create happiness. To boost the sense of Self worth and outgrow the role of victim in relationships. To promote the healthy undertaking of equal relationships, breaking up inferiority complexes.

Mind - Common Uses:

For those with feelings of inferiority due to suffering unkindness from people they cared for.

For those feeling "down-trodden" after relationship break-ups.

For the "underdog" in an ongoing relationship.

For feelings of sadness and hurt when loved ones have not been supportive.

The healing brings a focus back to one's inner beauty and specialness. To brighten the mind with positive feelings of Self esteem which looks towards future ideals of Love.

Healing Pathway to the Soul

Our inner Light is a Joy to see. Each being with its own unique brilliance, can be the creator of happiness for others. If this is unable to be appreciated by some, it does not change the fact of our radiance, - only to where we direct it.

Meditation Poem

Urchin Dryandra

All the talents and the gifts

I have to give

are there for all to see.

To share the beauty

from our bright Souls

creates a celebration.

Manifesting the Collective Ideal

**Positive Qualities
Key Words:**

wisdom

co-ordination

integrating

*taking
responsibility*

**Problem Target
Key Words:**

disillusioned

disheartened

criticizing

unrealistic

The essence of taking responsibility for the manifestation of a collective ideal. This includes shouldering the difficulties of personal interactions between group members, using integration, co-ordination and wisdom. To see clearly how to tackle problems between people. To accept the reality of group dynamics and retain idealism. Working with and engendering positivity and dealing effectively with negativity.

Mind - Common Uses:

For those who have given up on being able to work in groups of people, criticizing when things don't go right but not taking responsibility themselves. Not being prepared to do what is required to make the group function positively.

For those who have lost idealism about being able to solve the world's problems because of the obvious difficulties people have when working together.

For people focusing on the problems and not the solutions in group life.

For people feeling hopeless about having a harmonious family life.

For couples who can't find a way to combine their different needs and desires.

The healing brings a higher perspective on the problems involved in working together with people. Both the individual solutions and the collective solutions become something to work for, using co-ordination, wisdom and patience, to deal with every issue. The impasse is then broken and a sense of optimism and progress can be reclaimed. To inspire one to work constructively with the group to keep the flow and growth moving in a healthy direction despite problems with egos, dishonest communication and other common destructive elements.

215

Physical - Common Uses :

Used topically in body work to promote co-ordination and linking up of areas of the body that are functioning in an isolated way. Improves co-ordination of nerve impulses.
For example: a frozen shoulder that is not getting proper circulation and the carrying away of deposits, like uric acid. Erratic messages from the brain with sporadic uptake in the body in cases of cerebral palsy, muscular dystrophy, Muscle tremors/spasms, strokes. (use with Leafless Orchid)

Mind - Floral Acu-pressure

Psychological profile:
poor opinion of oneself, feeling useless and stupid.
Heart acu-point of the ear. (see Pg 255)
(see also Cowslip Orchid)

Physical - Floral Acu-pressure

Physical symptoms:
Hysteria, palpitation, arrhythmia.
The Heart acu-point of the ear. (see Pg 255)
(see also Cowslip Orchid)
Physical symptoms:
for pain and discomfort.
Spine, Neck and Joints acu-points of the ear.
(see Pg 256-259, 265-260)
(used with Leafless Orchid)
(see Dampiera, Macrozamia, Menzies Banksia, Purple Flag Flower)

Healing Pathway to the Soul

Every person has their individual talents and problems. Getting all these different characteristics to work together for a common purpose is an almighty challenge. There is a way when people keep the goal before them while never forgetting individual needs. By being committed to helping people through their individual blocks and difficulties, the entire group is enhanced and a true sense of unity prevails. They are then capable of achieving their collective goal and enjoying the daily collective experience as well.

Meditation Poem

Ursinia

Every person

is an imperfect bud

in a perfect garland

that delights the world

as a gift of beauty.

Making Bridges

Positive Qualities
Key Words:

fellowship

bridging

open

re-orientate

expression

Problem Target
Key Words:

isolated

retiring

lonely

sad

misunderstood

The essence of expressing and revealing oneself. Meeting the hearts of others. To re-orientate sensitivity towards reaching out to others and the efforts needed in order to bring about understanding. To inspire communication and interaction, breaking up isolation and loneliness.

Mind - Common Uses:

For those who feel sad, isolated and alone, that no one really knows them.
For those who feel misunderstood and so keep away from others for fear of being rejected.
For feelings of alienation within a family or group.
For those who are grieving the loss of a loved one and believe they will now always be alone.

The healing turns the person around to see how they can make contact with others, express themselves freely without concern for how they are received. Being open to people and welcoming them into friendships and relationships brings new opportunities for happiness.

Healing Pathway to the Soul

If all the people who were lonely sought out all the people who needed help, not one lonely or helpless person would remain. Outside our door the whole world waits breathlessly for us to make our move. Must we wait for the knock, or go out into the world?

Meditation Poem

Veronica

There, in every place on earth,

is a friend

waiting to be discovered.

I sing my welcome song

as I walk along.

To Love Again

Positive Qualities Key Words:

restoring capacity

regain Love

recovery

whole

Problem Target Key Words:

emotionally

shattered

trauma

overwhelmed

The essence to restore oneself and be open to the experience of Love. To calm flaring sensitivities and emotional pain, relieving stress. To heal the emotionally shattered, to speed the recovery of feelings, thus enabling a person to pass on through to the rest of their Life.

Mind - Common Uses:

For the person suffering from the shock of a relationship break-up.
For those recovering from an emotional trauma.
For feelings of being emotionally shattered, unable to imagine feeling whole and good again. To gather one's strength and emotional equipoise and move on with one's life is not an easy thing to do in such circumstances.

The healing greatly speeds the recovery from such traumas. It calms and heals the emotions and imbues one with vitality and strength. One is then able to open up to the possibilities to Love again.

Physical - Floral Acu-pressure

Physical symptoms:
insomnia, dream disturbed sleep, inflammation, pain.
Shenmen acu-point on the ear. (see Pg 263)
(see also Hybrid Pink Fairy Orchid, Yellow Flag Flower, Purple Flag Flower, Cowkicks, Reed Triggerplant, Pink Fountain Triggerplant, see which combination or single flower applies to the situation)

Healing Pathway to the Soul

We can never underestimate the power of an emotional experience, especially in affairs of the heart. Our attachments to people can leave us open to trauma and leave us stunned. Through healing we can reach the core of our being and restore our faith in Love and people, and with new learned wisdom appreciate Love again.

Meditation Poem

Violet Butterfly

My Love nature was bruised and sad.

The violet colours of the dawn

renewed my hope

and bathed in that light

I Love again.

Worldly Wise

Positive Qualities Key Words:

alert

wise

mature

aware

responsible

The essence to steady the mind-focus and inspire facing up to the realities and consequences of choices. To be alert to all aspects of a situation and be prepared to take them into account. To have a mature and wise view of Life. To avoid unnecessary dangers.

Problem Target Key Words:

naive

scattered

vulnerable

avoid facing reality

Mind - Common Uses:

For those showing shallow naivety.

For teenagers who don't realize how vulnerable they make themselves to harm.

The person who doesn't like to think of the consequences of their behaviour, the result being that they are irresponsible.

For those who make fun of caution. Rebellion against caution.

For people who act scattily with a tendency to pass off important issues.

For those who leap into situations they are not ready for.

The mind which is steady, alert and aware helps to keep us out of harm's way. If parts of our nature do not like some of the realities of life, a scattered, mindless approach to important issues can be a way to avoid facing up to the truth. Luck is then the only thing standing between us and the consequences of choices and actions, (or inaction), we make. Naivety, linked to lack of awareness or irresponsibility, can expose a person and those close to them to unnecessary trauma.

This healing steadies the mind-focus to face up to the realities of life. The wisdom of good choices and the consequences of bad choices becomes clear. When this is achieved fun and adventure will be rewarding experiences without hidden dangers.

Healing Pathway to the Soul

It is a much happier Path to look for wisdom than to ignore peril. To look for wisdom and understanding of Life allows us much more freedom, and positive consequences. To be foolhardy and ignore peril, hoping nothing bad will happen, leaves us in a state where we will have to learn through pain. Naivete will not protect us from the consequences of our choices. However wisdom will give us the choice of which difficulties we are ready for, and which we need to avoid.

Meditation Poem

Wattle

Today I know but little

tomorrow I will know more.

Each step will bring me closer

to understanding

what lies beneath so many veils and layers,

which keys fit in which doors.

Unity of Being

Positive Qualities
Key Words:

connected

whole

re-integrated

clear headed

Problem Target
Key Words:

vague

disconnected

directionless

faint

stress

fear

The essence to regain control of all aspects of one's being. To re-integrate the subtle and more physical levels into a functioning whole again. To be wholeheartedly involved in one's activities because of uniting desires with action. To give greater concentration, and relief from feeling vague. To strengthen the mind-body connection after stress and trauma.

Mind - Common Uses:

For those who are half heartedly involved in their life activities.

For those who are not fully accepting of their life and drift along without a strong mental direction.

For those who mechanically go about their day, but their mind is not on it.

For those who have suffered a shock or trauma, with intense fear.

For those who feel disconnected from life, ungrounded and easily swept away by strong events.

For those who have weak mind-body connections, and are prone to being vague and muddled.

For those anxious that they are losing control of their mind under stress.

For fears from unknown origin.

The healing re-integrates the mind and body into a whole which is again resilient and dynamic.

Physical - Common Uses:

Used topically on the forehead for drowsiness/disorientation. (use with Cowkicks)

Physical - Floral Acu-pressure

Physical symptoms:
fainting, delirium, effects of anaesthesia, losing consciousness.
Extra Six acu-point on the head. (see Pg 272)
Apply drops of the essence directly to point every ten minutes.

Healing Pathway to the Soul

For the Soul to be successful in physical incarnation the mind and body need to have a harmonious and compatible relationship. The harmonizing and integration of mind and body furthers the Soul's ability to achieve its end. This is the reason why yogis practice Hatha Yoga. We must be whole to have vitality and to live properly within our Life, making progress on all levels simultaneously. Every part of our body, mind and Soul needs feeding and nurturing, and they then work together to create the sense of well being.

Meditation Poem

West Australian Smokebush

I am at one.

My mind holds my body

in a loving embrace,

my Soul wraps the Light around.

There is radiance in my being

so vitally complete.

To See Through the Mist

**Positive Qualities
Key Words:**

clarity

perspective

observing

objectivity

**Problem Target
Key Words:**

tangled up

preconceived ideas

reacting

unclear

The essence of clarification of complexities through calmly observing and seeing Life as it is. To enhance decision making. To maintain equipoise, consistency and direction in Life. To develop a broad and fresh perspective which takes in the different dynamics of time, place and person, even in messy situations. Seeing through the tangled events to what is really happening.

Mind - Common Uses:

For those having the inability to discern between complexities, having a lack of clarity in decision making, or being too caught in preconceived ideas.
For those with knotty problems that cause confusion and stress.
For those who find themselves reacting to isolated incidents rather than having an overview of the situation that is creating them.

This healing stimulates us to look at the overall situation, observing and acting accordingly, rather than reacting to the many incidences that are borne out of the one situation. Clarity then leads to good decisions on how best to deal with events.

Mind - Floral Acu-pressure

Psychological profile:
Too many new ideas, too much input, chaos, inability to follow through or get things together.
Lung acu-point of the ear. (see Pg 261)

Psychological profile:
feeling mentally inept or stupid.
Forehead acu-point of the ear. (see Pg 253)
(see also Brachycome)

Psychological profile:
pushing ahead to hard and regardless of consequences, like wrecking their health, everything neglected except the pursuit of their goal.
Thyroid acu-point of the ear (see Pg 268)

Psychological profile:
Self righteous, judgmental, intolerant of other's faults. Tendency to take advantage from a position of strength - "I deserve the good things, I deserve to be treated well"
Liver acu-point of the ear (see Pg 261)

Physical - Floral Acu-pressure

Physical symptoms: cough, asthma.
Lung acu-point on the ear. (see Pg 261)
(see also Brachycome, Yellow Leschenaultia)

Physical symptoms: headache, dizziness, insomnia.
Forehead acu-point of the ear. (see Pg 253)
(see also Brachycome)

Physical symptoms: Hepatitis, hypochondriac pain, eye diseases.
Liver acu-point of the ear. (see Pg 261)
(see also Blue Leschenaultia)

Healing Pathway to the Soul

When we can't clearly see what is happening it is easy just to react on impulses or become engulfed in trouble and be unable to be part of the solution. To have clarity of mind, being able to see the big picture, enables us to work for the most positive of outcomes.

Meditation Poem

White Eremophila

> Like an eagle I can look down
>
> and see the landscape,
>
> every person, every feeling,
>
> how streams lead to rivers
>
> and rivers to the sea.

Positive Qualities Key Words:

Spiritual

perspective

emotional

purification

inner calm

meditation

Problem Target Key Words:

desires denied

frustrated

caught

lack of vision

Seeker of the Soul

The essence of uncovering the deepest spiritual core. The essence of tranquillity that encourages pulling back the layers to reach the Soul level. To inspire using the higher Self to integrate and respond to Life from the most Universal perspective possible for one's evolution at the time, rather than one's personal perspective. Helpful for spiritual practices such as meditation.

Mind - Common Uses:

For the spiritual aspirant, meditator.
For a person suddenly facing a grim challenge.
For those unable to find inner calm.
For those feeling the need for a new and wiser perspective during times of difficulty.
For those whose aspirations or desires are denied fulfilment, emotional frustration and irritation set in. When this happens over a period of time they can end up feeling that life is unfair and this type of thinking further compounds the problem.

The healing settles the troubled waters of the emotions. One is able to see the beauty and love in Life beyond the confines of personal desires, likes and dislikes. Instead of getting frustrated one goes with the flow and allows a whole new vista of beauty to be experienced and enjoyed. The essence stimulates desirelessness while enhancing the ability to enjoy what Life provides in the here and now. It spiritually stimulates inner contentment and desirelessness.

Mind - Floral Acu-pressure

Psychological profile: over-sexual, strong desire for excitement and fun.
External Genitalia acu-point on the ear. (see Pg 254)
(use with Purple Nymph Waterlily)

Physical - Floral Acu-pressure

Physical symptoms: impotence, sexual frigidity.
External Genitalia acu-point on the ear. (see Pg 254)
(used with Purple Nymph Waterlily)
(see also Macrozamia and Balga (impotence))

Healing Pathway to the Soul

The Soul waits patiently for the restless mind to settle, the mind pulling our being here and there in a quest for fulfilment. Still the Soul waits. The mind's desires, when not focused on the Universal goal, lead us on many a frustrating pilgrimage. Within us the clear lake of Consciousness remains unassailed, to reach that core, the mind must surrender to the Soul.

Meditation Poem

White Nymph Waterlily

I rise through the mud of desire,

up into the water, air and sun

I arise

pristine and white

facing the Light

resting in tranquillity.

230

Positive Qualities Key Words:

sustaining

maintaining Love

rise above

purpose

Problem Target Key Words:

overwhelmed

sadness

anguish

introversion

aversion

The Care Giver

The essence to bring Love and caring to the darkest corners of the Universe without being devastated by the intensive, and sometimes overwhelming, suffering around you. For those who seek to make this planet a better place for all. To inspire those in the caring professions and in volunteer service, engendering a higher perspective on the purpose of pain in the journey of the Soul.

Mind - Common Uses:

For those with humanitarian aims who find themselves unable to cope with the anguish that they experience. This can lead to sadness and introversion.

For those who are sensitive to the pain of others and feel too paralysed to be able to change the situation. For the care giver who can't go on. For those with high ideals who have been abused and now find life intolerably hard.

The healing enables a person to empathize with the suffering of others without being thrown off course, or unduly disturbed by insensitive acts. When this happens the person is able to relieve suffering and not get burnt out in the process. Being able to continue such work is essential for a better world.

Healing Pathway to the Soul

Suffering seems so senseless, we feel there cannot be any good in it. It makes us feel that the world is unfriendly and inflicts pain randomly. When we are seeing the sufferings of others we can feel so helpless, even when we are doing everything we can. At that point the highest spiritual perspective will help us through, not by cutting us off from the painful realities, but by seeing the benevolent processes of Life working through to reach the phases of regeneration and renewal. With this understanding we can better help and speed these processes, all the while restoring our ideals in the goodness of Life.

Meditation Poem

White Spider Orchid

I give you a world of Love

full of sweet embraces.

People sharing a fellowship

of supporting one another.

Every broken heart heals,

—bathed in the Light.

Positive Qualities
Key Words:

explore

open

courage

happiness

Problem Target
Key Words:

over cautious

pessimistic

apprehensive

worry

The Spirit of Optimism

The essence of optimism and exploring new options. To find a balance between caution and courageous decision making. To be able to trust new opportunities despite unknown outcomes, so as not to stop oneself from experiencing Life.

Mind - Common Uses:

For those who wish to be more open to the positive side of Life and feel joy again.

For those who tend to be fatalistic and negative about Life in general, and so miss vital opportunities for happiness. (Sometimes called a "kill-joy")

For those with tendencies to worry and be pessimistic.

For those who can't find a good word to say about anyone.

For a complaining attitude.

For those being apprehensive about how everything is, or whether things are working out, leading to melancholy or depressive states.

For older people who can't feel positive about Life any more and have the habit of running everything down.

The healing brings a new optimistic embrace of Life, with attitudes that promote positivity and happy outcomes.

Mind - Floral Acu-pressure

Psychological profile:
Anxiety, worried about what could happen.
Sympathetic Nerve acu-point on the ear. (see Pg 267)

Physical - Floral Acu-pressure

Physical symptoms: Diseases of digestive and circulatory systems.
Sympathetic Nerve acu-point on the ear. (see Pg 267)
(see also Blue China Orchid)

Healing Pathway to the Soul

It is so easy to get caught in seeing what is wrong in everything. This focus creates a gravity that sucks all positivity into it like a black hole. To pull out of this takes a lot of healing and strength. Far better never to indulge in such a frame of mind in the first place, and if we find any of these tendencies surfacing, deal with them straight away before they damage ourselves and others.

Meditation Poem

Wild Violet

Yes is a word warm and inviting.

Laughter is a feeling

that brings people together.

Joy is a precious gift

that waits to be opened.

To Realize a Dream

**Positive Qualities
Key Words:**

belief in success

optimism

renewed idealism

**Problem Target
Key Words:**

fatalistic

disheartened

unsure

sad

defeatist

The essence of believing in success. To face new goals without fear of inevitable failure. Not to lose heart, but rekindle the desire to forge ahead with ideals, even when there is struggle and difficulty. Helpful during long, tiring and seemingly pointless phases during the journey to reach one's aspirations.

Mind - Common Uses:

For those who feel they cannot get ahead with what they are wanting to achieve. They get stuck where they are, seeing only more problems and hardship if they move ahead.

For the sad, exhausted idealist.

For those feeling disheartened and unsure of the way ahead, hesitating to go forward.

For loss of inspiration during a long and hard endeavour.

For when the load one carries in life becomes too much, too heavy, too burdensome and there is a sense of inevitable failure to reach the treasured goals one is striving for. One becomes stuck and unable to cope which makes the situation worse.

The healing gives the inspiration, strength and vitality to get on top of things and conquer, no matter how weary one feels. One then deals with things one step at a time and is not overwhelmed by the magnitude of what one thinks is needed to be achieved. There is a sense of detachment from the day to day difficulties, yet a renewed enthusiasm to deal with them.

235

Mind - Floral Acu-pressure

Psychological profile: feeling overburdened, one turns a blind eye to issues that are potentially problematic.
Diaphragm acu-point on the ear. (see Pg) 252

Physical - Floral Acu-pressure

Physical symptoms: hiccups, jaundice.
Diaphragm acu-point on the ear. (see Pg) 252
(see also Black Kangaroo Paw)

Healing Pathway to the Soul

What does it take never to give up on our most cherished objectives, our deepest longings inspired by a vision of Love? To keep our eyes on the goal while utilizing all the facets of our being to overcome any obstacles. These can come in all shapes and sizes, can seem never ending, and yet behind every road block is the possibility to plumb the depths of our inner resources and claim new potential.

Meditation Poem

Woolly Banksia

The prize is always mine

even as I reach for it.

It has been there within me

for countless time.

Feeding me with the vigour

to go on until it is in my hand.

The Spirit of Humility

**Positive Qualities
Key Words:**

Self perspective

humility

objectivity

**Problem Target
Key Words:**

dramatic

exaggerating

self orientated

The essence of higher perspective and humility. To avoid the traps of glamour and self importance so that Life is seen with objectivity. To maintain forward progress without distracting oneself with dramas. To see the relevance of central issues. To integrate the personality and the Soul, the personal "i" with the spiritual "I".

Mind - Common Uses:

For those who tend to exaggerate and create a focus of attention on themselves.

For those with an inability to see themselves in perspective to their real importance, unable to maintain a balanced view that isn't orientated on themselves.

For the drama queen, the vocal "do-gooder"

For people whose feeling of self importance becomes the central focus for living. When, over time, they don't get the respect or adulation they desire, they become listless and vague, retreating mentally and emotionally to where their illusions of self importance can be satisfied.

This healing takes one on a journey of self-forgetfulness. One feels the Love, the power and genius of the Universal Oneness and realizes each of us are just one small unit of consciousness in the significant Universal flow of Love.

Healing Pathway to the Soul

To integrate the personal "i" and the spiritual "I" is the purpose of spiritual endeavour. The personal "i" is always caught up with its own importance and abilities, and the spiritual "I" is preoccupied with seeing itself as a part of the Universal body of Life. This understanding enables the individual to see themselves in an enlightened perspective, that is, the Universe can exist without their support, but they cannot exist without the support of the Universe. This is the true spirit of humility.

Meditation Poem

Woolly Smokebush

Soul, Mind and Form

together are my Life.

The vast array of colours of which I am a part,

make up the Universe

complementing each other

making one picture, one piece of art.

*Positive Qualities
Key Words:*

tolerance

encouraging

understanding

teaching

*Problem Target
Key Words:*

hard

perfectionist

impatient

chastising

The Value of Mistakes

The essence of tolerance and understanding. The realization that there is value in making mistakes, because one can learn from them, especially when guided by a person of sincerity and benevolence. To be sensitive and seek to teach gently, not to judge harshly, either oneself or others.

Mind - Common Uses:

For the hard task master.
For those who don't like seeing mistakes and tend to take over and do things themselves.
For the parent or boss who doesn't have enough patience to calmly show where a person has gone wrong or is inadequate in what they are doing.
For those who set a very high standard for themselves and others which doesn't allow for the learning curve of errors. When mistakes occur or things go wrong they see it as failure, and chastise themselves or the people involved.

The healing inspires the mind to have a nurturing and calm reaction when things go wrong and not be sharp and critical. Being positive and encouraging inspires oneself, and others in the situation, to tackle problems enthusiastically, learning how to do it better and better all the time.

Healing Pathway to the Soul

The Soul is continually learning from "so called" mistakes, and defining itself as it journeys onwards. The beauty of making mistakes, and the reassessment of why and how it happened, is a vital component in the evolution of consciousness. Focus and achieving can be taken on fully without having to lose the sweeter states of patience, tenderness, carefreeness and joviality. In fact these states make the focus rewarding in the everyday and not only when the task is achieved, with the added bonus that people around you can enjoy the experience as well.

Meditation Poem

Yellow & Green Kangaroo Paw

A perfect job

was not achieved

but the wisdom gained

was food for my Soul

Thank you.

Positive Qualities
Key Words:

concentration

study

calm

focus

Problem Target
Key Words:

over active

scattered

restless

shallow

distracted

To Still the Mind

The essence to calm, still and centre the mind. To inspire deeper concentration and contemplation. To help one focus and follow a thought through calmly, and not be distracted.

Mind - Common Uses:

For those with over active minds, who find their thoughts get easily scattered.
For those who are easily distracted.
For the student who finds study difficult because their mind is restless or unfocussed.

The healing brings a calming and centering of the mind, which can then work with one's direction of thought or activity to achieve satisfying results.

Mind - Floral Acu-pressure

Psychological profile:
scattered mind, difficulty in concentration. don't know what they are
doing, all over the place.
Thyroid acu-point on the ear. (see Pg 268)

Healing Pathway to the Soul

The ancient Sanskrit word "Manusa" was used for human beings,
"man" = mind, "usa" = being, thus describing humans as Mind
Beings. The mind is our main instrument, through it we take the
journey which our body must follow and our Soul observes. From a
calm centre of the Soul, we need to be able to focus and direct the
mind, thus utilizing this instrument skilfully so the Path we take is
straight and progress always assured.

Meditation Poem

Yellow Boronia

The butterflies of thought

rest on the flower of Peace.

Together they slowly fan their wings

then become still,

contemplating Life's breezes.

Positive Qualities Key Words:

Self recognition

positivity

Self esteem

contentment

Problem Target Key Words:

under valued

inferiority complex

unaccepted

depressed

The Recognition of Self

The essence to encourage the realization that the first and most important opinion is the one you have about yourself. From this comes personal objectives for growth and expansion built on positivity and self assessment rather than outside recognition. To value one's Self.

Mind - Common Uses:

For those who need to be accepted by others because they feel inferior.
For those who are utilized by others and it is not recognized how valuable they are.
For those who do things for others, subconsciously motivated by the need to receive recognition from them. The lack of recognition makes them feel depressed.
For those feeling sad due to being taken for granted, but have set themselves up in the situation by undervaluing themselves.

The healing brings a feeling of inner contentment that dissolves the need for a recognition rating from others because their self assessment is positive, clear and strong.

Healing Pathway to the Soul

Inner peace comes from recognizing our own Self worth. A person secure in their sense of Self worth is impervious to the negative opinions of others. How the external world treats us and what we are internally do not necessarily reflect each other. It is the way in which we can properly assess and value ourselves and then how we project that reality that can create a thought wave that the world then positively responds to. This then ensures the external response and our internal reality do reflect each other.

Meditation Poem

Yellow Cone Flower

I am a being

of limitless wonder

of endless surprises

of flowing potential

of inner Joy.

The Carefree Spirit

carefree

light hearted

jovial

balanced

strength

**Problem Target
Key Words:**

stressed

sombre

glum

uptight

unprepared

The essence of light heartedness and calmness, despite rising pressure, so that inner peace and relationships with others do not suffer. To enjoy the garden of Life. To find fortitude and wisdom to handle stressful phases without life becoming one long hard chore.

Mind - Common Uses:

For those who lose the ability to be carefree, and life becomes more serious.

For those whose carefree attitude leaves them unprepared for a sudden test of resilience under stress.

For those who make life harder for themselves by being glum.

Mind - Floral Acu-pressure

Psychological profile:
feeling of going mad, losing one's grip on the mind.
Shenmen acu-point on the ear. (see Pg 263)
Psychological profile:
Feeling that one can't rely on others. Having to do things yourself because others will let you down. Independent, isolated.
The Small Intestine acu-point of the ear. (see Pg 264)

245

Physical - Floral Acu-pressure

Physical symptoms:
stress, insomnia, dream disturbed sleep, inflammation, pain.
Shenmen acu-point on the ear. (see Pg 256-259, 265-266)
(use with Purple Flag Flower) (see also Hybrid Pink Fairy Orchid, Pink
Fairy Orchid, Purple Flag Flower, Cowkicks, Pink Fountain
Triggerplant, Reed Triggerplant and Violet Butterfly)
Physical symptoms:
dyspepsia, palpitation
The Small Intestine acu-point of the ear. (see Pg 264)
(see also Happy Wanderer)

Healing Pathway to the Soul

Having Joy does not have to be solely for those times when
everything is going right, that we are on holidays, having time off
work, or that our dearly held plans are evidently succeeding. The
carefree Spirit can enjoy even the most difficult situation by seeing
the good will or humour imbedded in all events big or small, serious
or frivolous.

Meditation Poem

Yellow Flag Flower

I keep my smile with me

wherever I go

It helps me to see the Truth

to find the Light

and know the beauty in All.

Positive Qualities
Key Words:

open

listening

understanding

wisdom

learning

Problem Target
Key Words:

dismissive

intolerant

insensitive

impatient

arrogant

The Art of Listening

The essence of stimulating open-mindedness which then receives knowledge and concepts from others. To calm the mind, dispelling the illusion that we hear even when we do not listen. To become more capable of listening and learning wisdom.

Mind - Common Uses:

For those who do not listen properly, either uninterested in what is being said due to intellectual arrogance or being unable to open the mind enough to process the opinions of others.

For those who dismiss out of hand the thoughts of others.

For those who find it hard to understand what another person is meaning when they speak to them. They often miss the whole point of what is being communicated.

For those who have problems taking in information and remembering it.

For those who have problems remembering what they study.

For those who don't want to hear the ideas of others, for them it is a waste of time.

The "know it all".

For the person with "tunnel vision".

The healing brings a renewed appraisal of openness and tolerance. Sensitivity is enhanced and an appreciation of the thoughts and concepts of other people is developed. In learning not to assume that one does know, full expansion of consciousness is possible. Relationships with others automatically improve.

Mind - Floral Acu-pressure

Psychological profile:
Convinced about the correctness of one's ideas or knowledge. Feeling correct about one's conceptualization of the trend things should take or the way things should be.
Lung acu-point of the ear. (see Pg 261)
Psychological profile:
Not wanting to listen or accommodate another's ideas
Internal Ear acu-point of the ear. (see Pg 255)

Physical - Floral Acu-pressure

Physical symptoms: cough, asthma.
Lung acu-point on the ear. (see Pg 261)
(use with Brachycome) (see also White Eremophila)
Physical symptoms: tinnitus, impaired hearing.
Internal Ear acu-point of the ear. (see Pg 255)
(see also Geraldton Wax)

Healing Pathway to the Soul

The more we gain wisdom the more we recognize how open we must be to become wise. The mind is always looking for a concept, like a ledge, to clamber up on to and rest, saying "now I know". It is imperative to be aware there is always more to know and this knowledge and understanding comes from a myriad of sources. From the simplest Soul we can learn great Truths.

Meditation Poem

Yellow Leschenaultia

I open the door to hear your words

to know your mind. In its rich depths

I can see the Universe itself.

Floral Acu-maps
Ear (Auricular) Acu-points

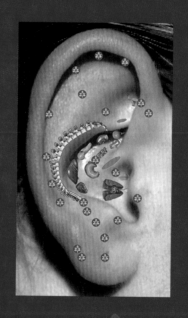

Flower Essences used on this point:

Macrozamia

Ribbon Pea

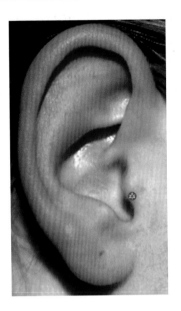

Mental /Emotional

Macrozamia
Confrontational, quick to respond in an aggressive manner to anything that seems threatening.

Ribbon Pea
Impulsive, panicky.

Physical
Macrozamia

Ribbon Pea
Hypotension, pulselessness, shock, asthma, inflammation.

Flower Essences used on this point:

Geraldton Wax

Purple Eremophila

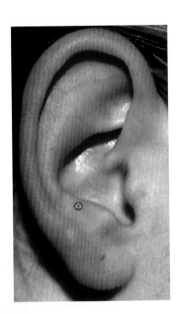

Mental /Emotional

Geraldton Wax
Feeling useless, helpless, unable to achieve.

Purple Eremophila
Looking for support from others, failing in one's own endeavor because there is no support from others. Feeling let down.

Physical

Geraldton Wax
Purple Eremophila
Headache, vertigo.

250

**Flower Essences
used on this point:**

Balga

Start's Spider
Orchid

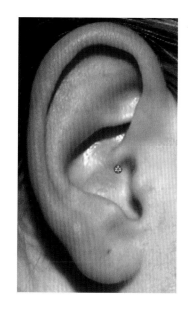

Mental /Emotional

Balga
Independent, self willed, does as
one pleases.

Start's Spider Orchid
Dependency.

Physical

Balga
Start's Spider Orchid
Nausea, vomiting.

**Flower Essences
used on this point:**

Red Beak Orchid

Red & Green
Kangaroo Paw

Start's Spider
Orchid

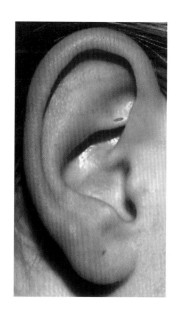

Mental /Emotional

Red Beak Orchid
Start's Spider Orchid
Energy and drive to fulfill one's
desires, no energy to fulfill one's
responsibilities.

Red Beak Orchid
Red & Green Kangaroo Paw
Unfulfilled desires, a frustrated
angry disposition.

Physical

Red Beak Orchid
Red & Green Kangaroo Paw
Start's Spider Orchid
Constipation, diarrhoea.

251

Flower Essences used on this point:

Black Kangaroo Paw

Woolly Banksia

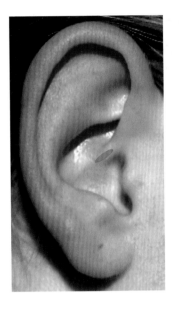

Mental /Emotional

Black Kangaroo Paw
Feeling overburdened, one becomes aggressive and insensitive in the pursuit of solutions.

Woolly Banksia
Due to feeling overburdened, one turns a blind eye to issues that are potentially problematic.

Physical

Black Kangaroo Paw
Woolly Banksia
Hiccups, jaundice.

Flower Essences used on this point:

Hybrid Pink Fairy Orchid

Red Leschenaultia

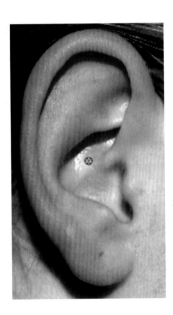

Mental /Emotional

Hybrid Pink Fairy Orchid
Feeling of wanting to be left alone, oversensitive towards others, overreacting to people, unable to maintain perspective.

Red Leschenaultia
Feeling self sufficient, not needing anyone, not wanting to share with others.

Physical

Hybrid Pink Fairy Orchid
Red Leschenaultia
Duodenal ulcer, pylorospasm.

*Flower Essences
used on this point:*

Cowslip Orchid

Red Beak Orchid

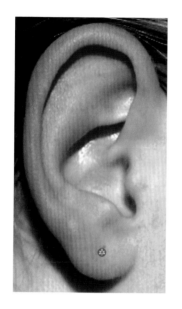

Mental /Emotional

Cowslip Orchid
Mind drawn too quickly onto anything in their surroundings, too externally concentrated, overly alert.

Red Beak Orchid
Can't care about things, drifting along.

Physical

Cowslip Orchid
Red Beak Orchid
Eye diseases, eye strain, problems focussing.

*Flower Essences
used on this point:*

Brachycombe

White Eremophila

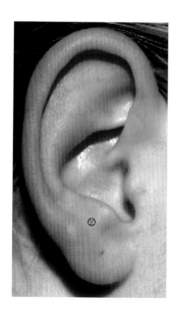

Mental /Emotional

Brachycombe
Intellectual arrogance.

White Eremophila
Feeling mentally inept or stupid.

Physical

Brachycombe
White Eremophila
Headache, dizziness, insomnia.

**Flower Essences
used on this point:**

Rabbit Orchid

Reed Triggerplant

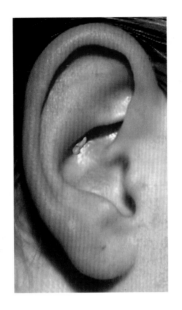

Mental /Emotional

Rabbit Orchid
Easy, fun loving, lack of
responsibility.

Reed Triggerplant
Oversensitive, inability to stand up
for oneself, weakness.

Physical

Rabbit Orchid
Reed Triggerplant
Pancreatitis, dyspepsia, diseases of
bile duct.

**Flower Essences
used on this point:**

Balga

Macrozamia

Purple Nymph
Waterlily

White Nymph
Waterlily

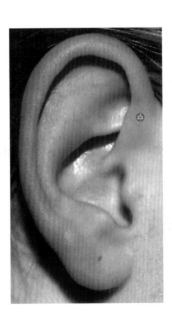

Mental /Emotional

Balga
Macrozamia
Sexual frigidity, aversion to
sexuality.

Purple Nymph Waterlily

White Nymph Waterlily
Over sexual, strong desire for
excitement and fun.

Physical

Macrozamia
Balga
Purple Nymph Waterlily
White Nymph Waterlily
Impotence, Sexual frigidity.

254

Flower Essences
ed on this point:

Cowslip Orchid

Ursinia

Cowkicks

Pink Fountain

Triggerplant

Purple Enamel

Orchid

eed Triggerplant

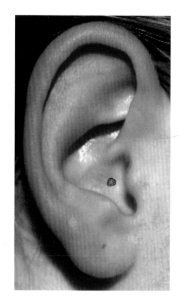

Mental /Emotional

Cowslip Orchid
Superiority complex, dictatorial

Ursinia
Poor opinion of oneself, feeling
useless and stupid.

Physical

Cowslip Orchid
Ursinia
Hysteria, palpitation, arrhythmia.

Cowkicks
Pink Fountain Triggerplant
Purple Enamel Orchid
Reed Triggerplant
Energy loss.

Flower Essences
d on this point:

Geraldton Wax

Yellow
Leshenaultia

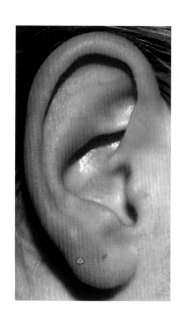

Mental /Emotional

Geraldton Wax
Over accommodating other's
opinions or ideas, listening too
much to others.

Yellow Leshenaultia
Not wanting to listen or
accommodate another's ideas

Physical

Geraldton Wax
Yellow Leshenaultia
Tinnitus, impaired hearing.

255

***Flower Essences
used on this point:***

Dampiera

Leafless Orchid

Macrozamia

Menzies Banksia

Purple Flag Flower

Ursinia

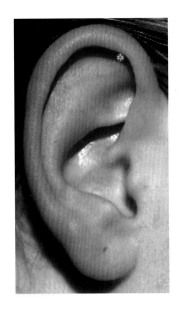

Physical
For pain in ankle/toe area.

Dampiera
Due to surrounding soft tissue being tight and rigid.

Leafless Orchid
Due to sluggish healing response.

Macrozamia
Due to poor fluid regulation.

Menzies Banksia
Due to cellular level pain memory.

Purple Flag Flower
Due to soft tissue stress and pressure build up.

Ursinia
Due to lack of coordination between body functions or parts.

***Flower Essences
used on this point:***

Dampiera

Leafless Orchid

Macrozamia

Menzies Banksia

Purple Flag Flower

Ursinia

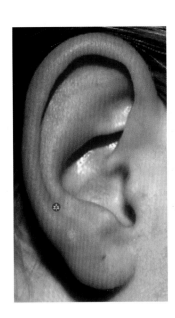

Physical
For pain in clavicle area.

Dampiera
Due to surrounding soft tissue being tight and rigid.

Leafless Orchid
Due to sluggish healing response.

Macrozamia
Due to poor fluid regulation.

Menzies Banksia
Due to cellular level pain memory.

Purple Flag Flower
Due to soft tissue stress and pressure build up.

Ursinia
Due to lack of coordination between body functions or parts.

Dampiera

Leafless Orchid

Macrozamia

Menzies Banksia

urple Flag Flower

Ursinia

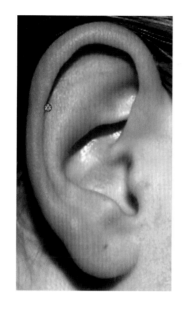

Physical
For pain in elbow area.

Dampiera
Due to surrounding soft tissue being tight and rigid.

Leafless Orchid
Due to sluggish healing response.

Macrozamia
Due to poor fluid regulation.

Menzies Banksia
Due to cellular level pain memory.

Purple Flag Flower
Due to soft tissue stress and pressure build up.

Ursinia
Due to lack of coordination between body functions or parts.

Dampiera

Leafless Orchid

Macrozamia

Menzies Banksia

urple Flag Flower

Ursinia

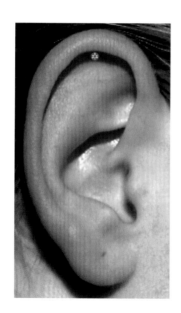
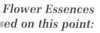

Physical
For pain in finger area.

Dampiera
Due to surrounding soft tissue being tight and rigid.

Leafless Orchid
Due to sluggish healing response.

Macrozamia
Due to poor fluid regulation.

Menzies Banksia
Due to cellular level pain memory.

Purple Flag Flower
Due to soft tissue stress and pressure build up.

Ursinia
Due to lack of coordination between body functions or parts.

257

***Flower Essences
used on this point:***

Dampiera

Leafless Orchid

Macrozamia

Menzies Banksia

Purple Flag Flower

Ursinia

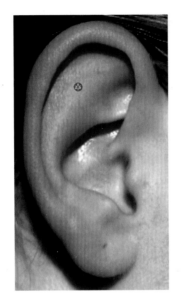

Physical
For pain in knee area.

Dampiera
Due to surrounding soft tissue being tight and rigid.

Leafless Orchid
Due to sluggish healing response.

Macrozamia
Due to poor fluid regulation.

Menzies Banksia
Due to cellular level pain memory.

Purple Flag Flower
Due to soft tissue stress and pressure build up.

Ursinia
Due to lack of coordination between body functions or parts.

***Flower Essences
used on this point:***

Dampiera

Leafless Orchid

Macrozamia

Menzies Banksia

Purple Flag Flower

Ursinia

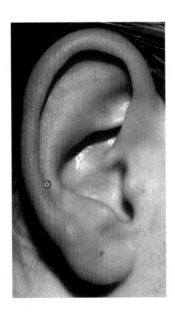

Physical
For pain in shoulder joint area.

Dampiera
Due to surrounding soft tissue being tight and rigid.

Leafless Orchid
Due to sluggish healing response.

Macrozamia
Due to poor fluid regulation.

Menzies Banksia
Due to cellular level pain memory.

Purple Flag Flower
Due to soft tissue stress and pressure build up.

Ursinia
Due to lack of coordination between body functions or parts.

*Flower Essences
used on this point:*

Dampiera

Leafless Orchid

Macrozamia

Menzies Banksia

Purple Flag Flower

Ursinia

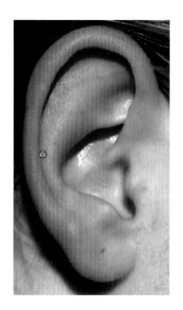

Physical
For pain in shoulder area.

Dampiera
Due to surrounding soft tissue being tight and rigid.

Leafless Orchid
Due to sluggish healing response.

Macrozamia
Due to poor fluid regulation.

Menzies Banksia
Due to cellular level pain memory.

Purple Flag Flower
Due to soft tissue stress and pressure build up.

Ursinia
Due to lack of coordination between body functions or parts.

*Flower Essences
used on this point:*

Dampiera

Leafless Orchid

Macrozamia

Menzies Banksia

Purple Flag Flower

Ursinia

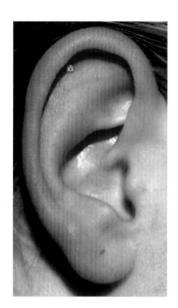

Physical
For pain in wrist area.

Dampiera
Due to surrounding soft tissue being tight and rigid.

Leafless Orchid
Due to sluggish healing response.

Macrozamia
Due to poor fluid regulation.

Menzies Banksia
Due to cellular level pain memory.

Purple Flag Flower
Due to soft tissue stress and pressure build up.

Ursinia
Due to lack of coordination between body functions or parts.

Flower Essences
used on this point:

Balga

Brown Boronia

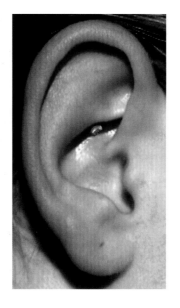

Mental /Emotional

Balga
Mentally confident, overly focused on implementing one's ideas. Insensitive and out of touch with one's environment and other people.

Brown Boronia
Mental confusion, too much to do. Worried and anxious, chaotic environment.

Physical

Balga
Brown Boronia
Tinnitis, impaired hearing, lumbago.

Flower Essences
used on this point:

Red Beak Orchid

Start's Spider Orchid

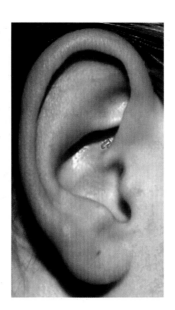

Mental /Emotional

Red Beak Orchid
Unmotivated, lazy.

Start's Spider Orchid
Desire to be left in peace, lethargic

Physical

Red Beak Orchid
Start's Spider Orchid
Constipation and/or diarrhoea.

260

*Flower Essences
used on this point:*

Macrozamia

Ribbon Pea

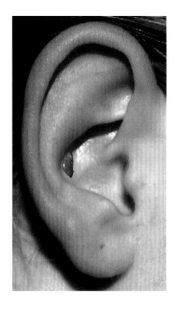

Mental /Emotional

Blue Leschenaultia
Psychological profile: possessive and/or avaricious due to insecurity/fear of being without.

White Eremophila
Self righteous, judgmental, intolerant of other's faults. Tendency to take advantage from a position of strength - "I deserve the good things, I deserve to be treated well"

Physical

Blue Leschenaultia
White Eremophila
Hepatitis, hypochondriac pain, eye diseases.

*Flower Essences
used on this point:*

Brachycombe

White Eremophila

*Yellow
Leschenaultia*

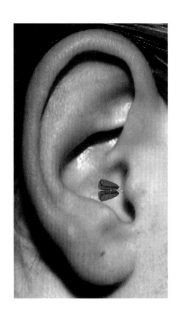

Mental /Emotional

Brachycombe
Yellow Leschenaultia
Convinced about the correctness of one's ideas or knowledge. Feeling correct about one's conceptualiz-ation of the trend things should take or the way things should be.

White Eremophila
Too many new ideas, too much input, chaos, inability to follow through or get things together.

Physical

Brachycombe
White Eremophila
Yellow Leschenaultia
Cough, asthma.

261

**Flower Essences
used on this point:**

Leafless Orchid

Pale Sundew

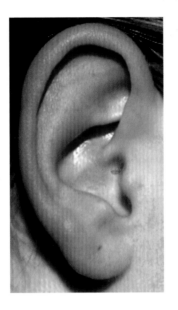

Mental /Emotional

Leafless Orchid
Lack of verbal control, saying things at inopportune moments, nervous eating habits, like picking at food.

Pale Sundew
Desire to trap and devour.

Physical

Leafless Orchid
Pale Sundew
Facial paralysis, ulceration of the mouth.

**Flower Essences
used on this point:**

Blue China Orchid

Cape Bluebell

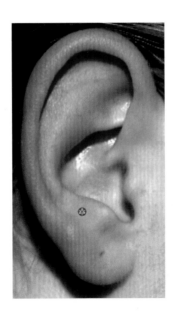

Mental /Emotional

Blue China Orchid
Avoidance of problems or unpleasantness, Over indulgence, a feeling of weakness.

Cape Bluebell
Over indulgence, a craving for fulfillment.

Physical

Blue China Orchid
Cape Bluebell
Headache, neurasthenia.

Flower Essences
used on this point:

Cowkicks

Hybrid Pink Fairy Orchid

Pink Fairy Orchid

Pink Fountain Triggerplant

Purple Flag Flower

Reed Triggerplant

Violet Butterfly

Yellow Flag

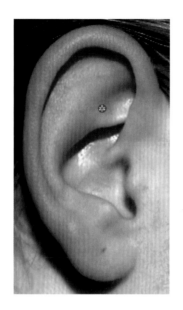

Mental /Emotional

Cowkicks
Hybrid Pink Fairy Orchid
Pink Fairy Orchid
Pink Fountain Triggerplant
Reed Trigger Plant
Violet Butterfly
Feeling of falling apart, unable to cope.

Purple Flag Flower
Yellow Flag Flower
Feeling of going insane, losing one's grip on one's mind.

Flower Essences
used on this point:

Cowkicks

Hybrid Pink Fairy Orchid

Pink Fairy Orchid

Pink Fountain Triggerplant

Purple Flag Flower

Reed Triggerplant

Violet Butterfly

Yellow Flag

263

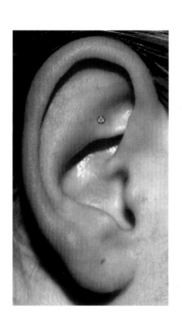

Physical

Cowkicks
Hybrid Pink Fairy Orchid
Pink Fairy Orchid
Pink Fountain Triggerplant
Purple Flag Flower
Reed Trigger Plant
Violet Butterfly
Yellow Flag Flower
Insomnia, dream-disturbed sleep, inflammation.

Flower Essences used on this point:

Happy Wanderer

Yellow Flag

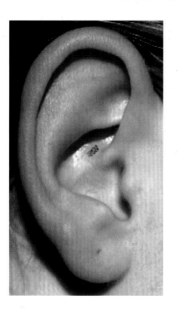

Mental /Emotional

Happy Wanderer
Looking for support from others, failing in one's own endeavors because there is no support from others. Feeling let down.

Yellow Flag   *Purple Eremophila*
Feeling that one can't rely on others. Having to do things yourself because others will let you down. Independent, isolated.

Physical

Happy Wanderer
Yellow Flag
Dyspepsia, palpitation.

Flower Essences used on this point:

Cape Bluebell

Pale Sundew

Swan River Myrtle

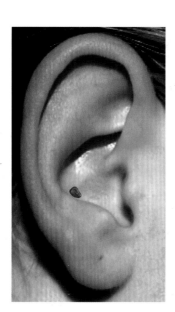

Mental /Emotional

Cape Bluebell
Pale Sundew
Perpetrating sadism, hatred.

Swan River Myrtle
Being abused, hurt, a victim of injustice or sadism.

Physical

Cape Bluebell
Pale Sundew
Swan River Myrtle
Abdominal distension.

***Flower Essences
used on this point:***

Dampiera

Leafless Orchid

Macrozamia

Menzies Banksia

Purple Flag Flower

Ursinia

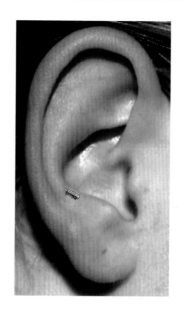

Physical

For pain in the cervical area of the spine.

Dampiera
Due to surrounding soft tissue being tight and rigid.

Leafless Orchid
Due to sluggish healing response.

Macrozamia
Due to poor fluid regulation.

Menzies Banksia
Due to cellular level pain memory.

Purple Flag Flower
Due to soft tissue stress and pressure build up.

Ursinia
Due to lack of coordination between body functions or parts.

***Flower Essences
used on this point:***

Dampiera

Leafless Orchid

Macrozamia

Menzies Banksia

Purple Flag Flower

Ursinia

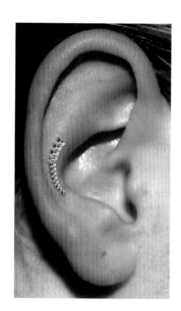

Physical

For pain in the thoracic area of the spine.

Dampiera
Due to surrounding soft tissue being tight and rigid.

Leafless Orchid
Due to sluggish healing response.

Macrozamia
Due to poor fluid regulation.

Menzies Banksia
Due to cellular level pain memory.

Purple Flag Flower
Due to soft tissue stress and pressure build up.

Ursinia
Due to lack of coordination between body functions or parts.

***Flower Essences
used on this point:***

Dampiera

Leafless Orchid

Macrozamia

Menzies Banksia

Purple Flag Flower

Ursinia

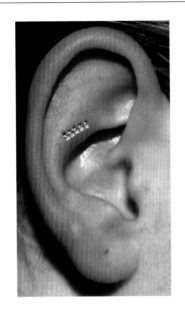

Physical
For pain in the lumbar area of the spine.

Dampiera
Due to surrounding soft tissue being tight and rigid.

Leafless Orchid
Due to sluggish healing response.

Macrozamia
Due to poor fluid regulation.

Menzies Banksia
Due to cellular level pain memory.

Purple Flag Flower
Due to soft tissue stress and pressure build up.

Ursinia
Due to lack of coordination between body functions or parts.

***Flower Essences
used on this point:***

Dampiera

Leafless Orchid

Macrozamia

Menzies Banksia

Purple Flag Flower

Ursinia

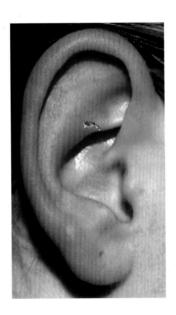

Physical
For pain in the sacral area of the spine.

Dampiera
Due to surrounding soft tissue being tight and rigid.

Leafless Orchid
Due to sluggish healing response.

Macrozamia
Due to poor fluid regulation.

Menzies Banksia
Due to cellular level pain memory.

Purple Flag Flower
Due to soft tissue stress and pressure build up.

Ursinia
Due to lack of coordination between body functions or parts.

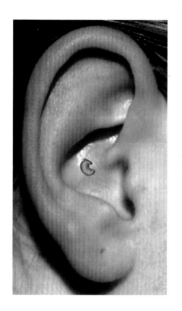

Mental /Emotional

Blue Leschenaultia
Attitudes of "I'm alright, life is going fine for me", but indifference to, or not wanting to be bothered about, other people's dilemmas or hardships.

Many Headed Dryandra
Feeling weak, wanting to pull away, can't cope, everything is too much.

Physical

Blue Leschenaultia
Many Headed Dryandra
Gastralgia, vomiting, dyspepsia.

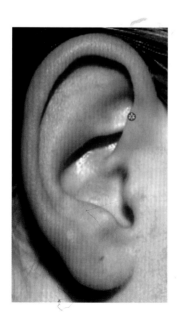

Mental /Emotional

Blue China Orchid
Strong desire to have excitement and fun.
Wild Violet
Anxiety, worry.

Physical

Blue China Orchid
Wild Violet
Diseases of digestive and circulatory systems.

267

Flower Essences used on this point:

Balga

Goddess Grasstree

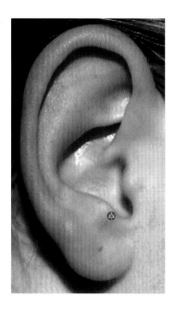

Mental /Emotional

Balga
Sexually under-confident, anxiety about one's sexual ability, impotence due to psychological problems.

Goddess Grasstree
Strong desire to have physical sexual experiences with another's body, overconfident, "stud" or "Macho" mentality that thinks "I'm good at this".

Physical

Balga
Goddess Grasstree
Premenstrual tension, abnormal menstruation, female hormone imbalance, menopause.

Flower Essences used on this point:

White Eremophila

Yellow Boronia

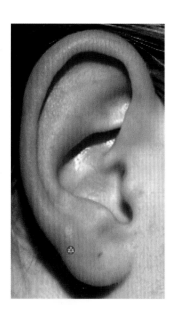

Mental /Emotional

White Eremophila
Pushing ahead too hard regardless of consequences, eg wrecking their health, everything neglected except the pursuit of their goal.

Yellow Boronia
Scattered mind, difficulty in concentration, don't know what they are doing, all over the place.

Flower Essences used on this point:

Giving Hands

Fringe Lily Twiner

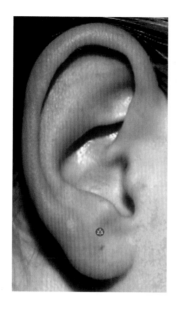

Mental /Emotional
Giving Hands
Indiscriminate giving, leaving oneself open to being exploited.

Fringe Lily Twiner
Jealousy, feeling you should have what your peers have, and resentful when you haven't.

Flower Essences used on this point:

Golden Glory Grevillea

Hairy Yellow Pea

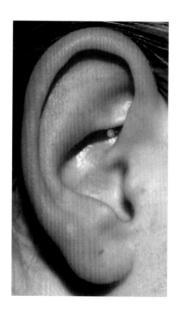

Mental /Emotional

Golden Glory Grevillea
Hairy Yellow Pea
Pretending to cope but masking the reality of one's inability to handle life internally and/or externally.

Hairy Yellow Pea
Believing one cannot achieve, feelings of being in a mess or devastated. Cannot see how things will work out.

Physical
Golden Glory Grevillea
Hairy Yellow Pea with
Enuresis, retention of urine.

269

Flower Essences
used on this point:

Cape Bluebell

Macrozamia

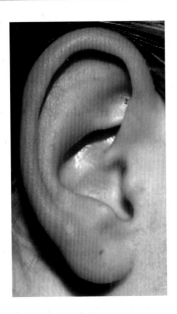

Mental /Emotional
Cape Bluebell
Desire for revenge, hatred.

Macrozamia
Desire for isolation, aversion to
people.

Physical
Cape Bluebell
Macrozamia
Irregular menstruation, leucorrhoea,
dysmenorrhoea, impotence,
nocturnal emission.

270

Floral Acu-maps
Body Acu-points

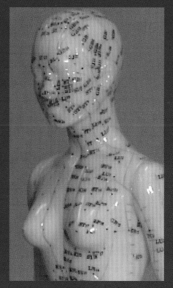

Flower Essences used on this point:

Leafless Orchid

Pink Trumpet

Mental /Emotional

Leafless Orchid
Giving out energy unwisely.

Pink Trumpet
Difficulty with mind focus and follow through.

Physical

Leafless Orchid
Energy depleted.

Baihui Point is found by taking a line from the bottom of the lobe to the top of the ear, then following that angle up onto the top of the head, on the midline.

Flower Essences used on this point:

West Australian Smokebush

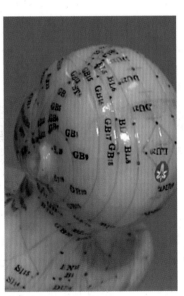

Mental /Emotional

West Australian Smokebush
Feelings of vagueness or anxiety.
Feelings of stress.
Lack of good mind/body connection.

Physical

West Australian Smokebush
After effects of anaesthesia.
Fainting, dizziness.

Extra Six point is found one thumb width*, (one "chun" or Chinese inch),
back from the Baihui point.

(*Note: the patient's thumb width)

Indexes

Jayasuriya, A. (1980) *Clinical Acupuncture*, Colombo: Medicina Alternativa, International

Beijing, Shanghai, and Nanjing Colleges of Traditional Chinese Medicine, Acupuncture Institute of the Academy of Traditional Chinese Medicine (1980)

Essentials of Chinese Acupuncture, Beijing: Foreign Languages Press